The So-Called
Human Race

BOOKS BY

BERT LESTON TAYLOR

A PENNY WHISTLE

THE SO-CALLED HUMAN RACE

THE EAST VIEW
(*Fall, 1922*)

And others in a uniform collected edition, to be ready later.

New York: Alfred · A · Knopf

The So-Called Human Race

by
Bert Leston Taylor

Arranged, with an Introduction, by
Henry B. Fuller

New York   1 9 2 2
Alfred · A · Knopf

Set up, electrotyped, and printed by J. J. Little & Ives Co., New York, N. Y.
Paper furnished by W. F. Etherington & Co., New York, N. Y.
Bound by the H. Wolff Estate, New York, N. Y.

MANUFACTURED IN THE UNITED STATES OF AMERICA

WORLD WITHOUT END

Once upon a summer's night
Mused a mischief-making sprite,
Underneath the leafy hood
Of a fairy-haunted wood.
Here and there, in light and shade,
Ill-assorted couples strayed:
"Lord," said Puck, in elfish glee,
"Lord, what fools these mortals be!"

Now he sings the self-same tune
Underneath an older moon.
Life to him is, plain enough,
Still a game of blind man's buff.
If we listen we may hear
Puckish laughter always near,
And the elf's apostrophe,
"Lord, what fools these mortals be!"

B. L. T.

Foreword

By Henry B. Fuller

Bert Leston Taylor (known the country over
as "B. L. T.") was the first of our day's
"colyumists"—first in point of time, and first in
point of merit. For nearly twenty years, with
some interruptions, he conducted "A Line-o'-Type
or Two" on the editorial page of the Chicago
Tribune. His broad column—broad by measure-
ment, broad in scope, and a bit broad, now and
again, in its tone—cheered hundreds of thousands at the breakfast-tables of the Middle West,
and on its trains and trolleys. As the "Column"
grew in reputation, "making the Line" became
almost a national sport. Whoever had a happy
thought, whoever could handily turn a humorous
paragraph or tune a pointed jingle, was only too
glad to attempt collaboration with B. L. T.
Others, possessing no literary knack, chanced it
with brief reports on the follies or ineptitudes of
the "so-called human race." Some of them
picked up their matter on their travels—these
were the "Gadders." Others culled oddities from
the provincial press, and so gave further scope

to "The Enraptured Reporter," or offered selected gems of *gaucherie* from private correspondence, and thus added to the rich yield of "The Second Post." Still humbler helpers chipped in with queer bits of nomenclature, thereby aiding the formation of an "Academy of Immortals"—an organization fully officered by people with droll names and always tending, as will become apparent in the following pages, to enlarge and vary its roster.

All these contributors, as well as many other persons who existed independently of the "Line," lived in the corrective fear of the "Cannery," that capacious receptacle which yawned for the trite word and the stereotyped phrase. Our language, to B. L. T., was an honest, living growth: deadwood, whether in thought or in the expression of thought, never got by, but was marked for the burning. The "Cannery," with its numbered shelves and jars, was a deterrent indeed, and anyone who ventured to relieve himself as "Vox Populi" or as a conventional versifier, did well to walk with care.

Over all these aids, would-be or actual, presided the Conductor himself, furnishing a steady framework by his own quips, jingles and philosophizings, and bringing each day's exhibit to an ordered unity. The Column was more than the sum of its contributors. It was the sum of units, original or contributed, that had been manipulated and brought to high effectiveness by a skilled hand and a nature wide in its sympathies and in its range of interests.

Taylor had the gift of opening new roads and of inviting a willing public to follow. Or, to put it another way, he had the faculty of making new moulds, into which his helpers were only too glad to pour their material. Some of these "leads" lasted for weeks; some for months; others persisted through the years. The lifted wand evoked, marshalled, vivified, and the daily miracle came to its regular accomplishment.

Taylor hewed his Line in precise accord with his own taste and fancy. All was on the basis of personal preference. His chiefs learned early that so rare an organism was best left alone to function in harmony with its own nature. The Column had not only its own philosophy and its own æsthetics, but its own politics: if it seemed to contravene other and more representative departments of the paper, never mind. Its conductor had such confidence in the validity of his personal predilections and in their identity with those of "the general," that he carried on things with the one rule of pleasing himself, certain that he should find no better rule for pleasing others. His success was complete.

His papers and clippings, found in a fairly

forward state of preparation, gave in part the necessary indications for the completion of this volume. The results will perhaps lack somewhat the typographical effectiveness which is within the reach of a metropolitan daily when utilized by a "colyumist" who was also a practical printer, and they can only approximate that piquant employment of juxtaposition and contrast which made every issue of "A Line-o'-Type or Two" a work of art in its way. But no arrangement of items from that source could becloud the essential nature of its Conductor: though "The So-Called Human Race" sometimes plays rather tartly and impatiently with men's follies and shortcomings, it clearly and constantly exhibits a sunny, alert and airy spirit to whom all things human made their sharp appeal.

The So-Called
Human Race

A LINE-O'-TYPE OR TWO

*Motto: Hew to the Line, let
the quips fall where they may.*

SIMPLE

MY readers are a varied lot;
  Their tastes do not agree.
A squib that tickles A is not
  At all the thing for B.

What's sense to J, is folderol
  To K, but pleases Q.
So, when I come to fill the Col,
  I know just what to do.

IT IS refreshing to find in the society columns an account of a quiet wedding. The conventional screams of a groom are rather trying.

A MAN will sit around smoking all day and his wife will remark: "My dear, aren't you smoking too much?" The doctor cuts him down to three cigars a day, and his wife remarks: "My dear, aren't you smoking too much?" Finally he chops off to a single after-dinner smoke, and when he lights up his wife remarks: "John, you do nothing but smoke all day long." Women are singularly observant.

[1]

NO DOUBT THERE ARE OTHERS.

Sir: A gadder friend of mine has been on the road so long that he always speaks of the parlor in his house as the lobby.   E. C. M.

WITH the possible exception of Trotzky, Mr. Hearst is the busiest person politically that one is able to wot of. Such boundless zeal! Such measureless energy! Such genius—an infinite capacity for giving pains!

ANCESTOR worship is not peculiar to any tribe or nation. We observed last evening, on North Clark street, a crowd shaking hands in turn with an organ-grinder's monkey.

"IN FACT," says an editorial on Uncongenial Clubs, "a man may go to a club to get away from congenial spirits." True. And is there any more uncongenial club than the Human Race? The service is bad, the membership is frightfully promiscuous, and about the only place to which one can escape is the library. It is always quiet there.

SIGN in the Black Hawk Hotel, Byron, Ill.: "If you think you are witty send your thoughts to B. L. T., care Chicago Tribune. Do not spring them on the help. It hurts efficiency."

AN OBSERVANT KANSAN.

[From the Emporia Gazette.]

The handsome clerk at the Harvey House makes this profound observation: Any girl will flirt as the train is pulling out.

THE GIRL OF THE PERIOD.

She formerly talked of the weather,
  The popular book, or the play;
    Her old line of chat
    Was of this thing or that
  In the fashions and fads of the day.

But now she discusses eugenics,
  And things that a pundit perplex;
    She knocks you quite flat
    With her new line of chat,
And her "What do you think about sex?"

"ARE we all to shudder at the name of Rabelais and take to smelling salts?" queries an editorial colleague. "Are we to be a wholly ladylike nation?" Small danger, brother. Human nature changes imperceptibly, or not at all. The objection to most imitations of Rabelais is that they lack the unforced wit and humor of the original.

A PICTURE of Dr. A. Ford Carr testing a baby provokes a frivolous reader to observe that when

[3]

the babies cry the doctor probably gives them a rattle.

WHAT DO YOU MEAN "ALMOST"!
[From the Cedar Rapids Republican.]

The man who writes a certain column in Chicago can always fill two-thirds of it with quotations and contributions. But that may be called success—when they bring the stuff to you and are almost willing to pay you for printing it.

WE'LL TELL THE PLEIADES SO.

Sir: "I'll say she is," "Don't take it so hard," "I'll tell the world." These, and other slangy explosives from our nursery, fell upon the sensitive auditory nerves of callers last evening. I am in a quandary, whether to complain to the missus or write a corrective letter to the children's school teachers, for on the square some guy ought to bawl the kids out for fair about this rough stuff —it gets my goat. J. F. B.

DID you think "I'll say so" was new slang? Well, it isn't. You will find it in Sterne's "Sentimental Journey."

FORMULA for accepting a second cigar from a man whose taste in tobacco is poor: "Thank you; the courtesy is not *all* yours."

[4]

A NUMBER of suicides are attributed to the impending conjunction of the planets and the menace of world-end. You can interest anybody in astronomy if you can establish for him a connection between his personal affairs and the movements of the stars.

WHERE 'VANGIE LIES.
Rondeau Sentimental to Evangeline, the Office Goat.

Where 'Vangie lies strown folios
Like Vallambrosan leaves repose,
   The sad, the blithe, the quaint, the queer,
   The good, the punk are scattered here—
A pile of poof in verse and prose.

And none would guess, save him who strows,
How much transcendent genius goes
   Unwept, unknown, into the smear
                Where 'Vangie lies.

With every opening mail it snows
Till 'Vangie's covered to her nose.
   Forgetting that she is so near,
   I sometimes kick her in the ear.
Then sundry piteous ba-a-a's disclose
                Where 'Vangie lies.

"THIS sale," advertises a candid clothier, "lasts only so long as the goods last, and that won't be very long."

THE SECOND POST.

(Letter from an island caretaker.)

Dear Sir: Your letter came. Glad you bought a team of horses. Hilda is sick. She has diphtheria and she will die I think. Clara died this eve. She had it, too. We are quarantined. Five of Fisher's family have got it. My wife is sick. She hain't got it. If this thing gets worse we may have to get a doctor. Them trees are budding good. Everything is O. K.

JUST as we started to light a pipe preparatory to filling this column, we were reminded of Whistler's remark to a student who was smoking: "You should be very careful. You know you might get interested in your work and let your pipe go out."

IT IS odd, and not uninteresting to students of the so-called human race, that a steamfitter or a manufacturer of suspenders who may not know the difference between the Declaration of Independence and the Constitution—who may not, indeed, know anything at all—is nevertheless a bubbly-fountain of political wisdom; whereas a writer for a newspaper is capable of emitting only drivel. This may be due to the greater opportunity for meditation enjoyed by suspender-makers and steamfitters.

JANESVILLE's Grand Hotel just blew itself on its Thanksgiving dinner. The menu included "Cheese a la Fromage."

"IT IS with ideas we shall conquer the world," boasts Lenine. If he needs a few more he can get them at the Patent Office in Washington, which is packed with plans and specifications of perpetual motion machines and other contraptions as unworkable as bolshevism.

HEARD IN THE BANK.

A woman from the country made a deposit consisting of several items. After ascertaining the amount the receiving teller asked, "Did you foot it up?" "No, I rode in," said she.

H. A. N.

THE fact that Abraham Lincoln, George Washington, and other great departed whose names are taken in vain every day by small-bore politicians, do not return and whack these persons over the heads with a tambourine, is almost—as Anatole France remarked in an essay on Flaubert —is almost an argument against the immortality of the soul.

HARPER'S WEEKLY refrains from comment on the shipping bill because, says its editor, "we have not been able to accumulate enough knowledge."

Well! If every one refrained from expressing an opinion on a subject until he was well informed the pulp mills would go out of business and a great silence would fall upon the world.

IT IS pleasant to believe the sun is restoring its expended energy by condensation, and that the so-called human race is in the morning of its existence; and it is necessary that the majority should believe so, for otherwise the business of the world would not get done. The happiest cynic would be depressed by the sight of humanity sitting with folded hands, waiting apathetically for the end.

PERHAPS the best way to get acquainted with the self-styled human race is to collect money from it.

TO A WELL-KNOWN GLOBE.

I would not seem to slam our valued planet,—
  Space, being infinite, may hold a worse;
Nor would I intimate that if I ran it
  Its vapors might disperse.

Within our solar system, or without it,
  May be a world less rationally run;
There may be such a geoid, but I doubt it—
  I can't conceive of one.

If from the time our sphere began revolving
    Until the present writing there had been
A glimmer of a promise of resolving
    The muddle we are in:

If we could answer "Whither are we drifting?"
    Or hope to wallow out of the morass—
I might continue boosting and uplifting;
    But as it is, I pass.

So on your way, old globe, wherever aiming,
    Go blundering down the endless slopes of space:
As far away the prospect of reclaiming
    The so-called human race.

Gyrate, old Top, and let who will be clever;
    The mess we're in is much too deep to solve.
Me for a quiet life while you, as ever,
    Continue to revolve.

"OUR editorials," announces the Tampa Tribune, "are written by members of the staff, and do not necessarily reflect the policy of the paper." Similarly, the contents of this column are written by its conductor and the straphangers, and have nothing whatever to do with its policy.

"WHAT, indeed?" as Romeo replied to Juliet's query. And yet Ralph Dilley and Irene Pickle were married in Decatur last week.

HE WAS heard to observe, coming from the theater into the thick of the wind and snow: "God help the rich; the poor can sleep with their windows shut."

[9]

WE have received a copy of the first issue of The Fabulist, printed in Hingham Centre, Mass., and although we haven't had time to read it, we like one of its ideas. "Contributions," it announces, "must be paid for in advance at space rates."

THE viewpoint of Dr. Jacques Duval (interestingly set forth by Mr. Arliss) is that knowledge is more important than the life of individual members of the so-called human race. But even Duval is a sentimentalist. He believes that knowledge is important.

AMONG reasonable requests must be included that of the Hotel Fleming in Petersburg, Ind.: "Gentlemen, please walk light at night. The guests are paying 75 cents to sleep and do not want to be disturbed."

WE have recorded the opinion that the Lum Tum Lumber Co. of Walla Walla, Wash., would make a good college yell; but the Wishkah Boom Co. of Wishkah, Wash., would do even better.

SOME ONE was commiserating Impresario Dippel on his picturesque assortment of griefs. "Yes," he said, "an impresario is a man who has trouble. If he hasn't any he makes it."

WHAT is the use of expositions of other men's philosophic systems unless the exposition is made lucid and interesting? Philosophers are much like certain musical critics: they write for one another, in a jargon which only themselves can understand.

O SHADE of Claude Debussy, for whom the bells of hell or heaven go tingalingaling (for wherever you are it is certain there are many bells—great bells, little bells, bells in high air, and bells beneath the sea), how we should rejoice that the beautiful things which you dreamed are as a book that is sealed to most of those who put them upon programmes; for these do not merely play them badly, they do not play them at all. Thus they cannot be spoiled for us, nor can our ear be dulled; and when the few play them that understand, they are as fresh and beautiful as on the day when first you set them down.

"THE increase in the use of tobacco by women," declares the Methodist Board, "is appalling." Is it not? But so many things are appalling that it would be a relief to everybody if a board, or commission, or other volunteer organization were to act as a shock-absorber. Whenever an appalling situation arose, this group could be appalled for the rest of us. And we, knowing that the board would be properly appalled, should not have to worry.

AD of a Des Moines baggage transfer company: "Don't lie awake fearing you'll miss your train—we'll attend to that." You bet they do.

THE president of the Printing Press and Feeders' (sic) union estimates that a family in New York requires $2,362 a year to get by. Which sets us musing on the days of our youth in Manchester, N. H., when we were envied by the others of the newspaper staff because we got $18 a week. We lived high, dressed expensively (for Manchester), and always had money for Wine and Song. How did we manage it? Blessed if we can remember.

THE soi-disant human race appears to its best advantage, perhaps its only advantage, in work. The race is not ornamental, nor is it over-bright, having only enough wit to scrape along with. Work is the best thing it does, and when it seeks to avoid this, its reason for existence disappears.

"WHERE," asks G. N., "can I find the remainder of that beautiful Highland ballad beginning—

'I canna drook th' stourie tow,
    Nor ither soak my hoggie:
Hae cluttered up the muckle doon,
    An' wow but I was voggie.'"

WOMEN regard hair as pianists regard technic: one can't have too much of it.

[12]

THE demand for regulation of the sale of wood alcohol reminds Uncle Henry of Horace Greeley's remark when he was asked to subscribe to a missionary fund "to save his fellow-man from going to hell." Said Hod, "Not enough of them go there now."

A FEW lines on the literary page relate that Edith Alice Maitland, who recently died in London, was the original of "Alice In Wonderland." Lewis Carroll wrote the book for her, and perhaps read chapters to her as he went along. Happy author, happy reader! If the ordering of our labors were entirely within our control we should write exclusively for children. They are more intelligent than adults, have a quicker apprehension, and are without prejudices. In addressing children, one may write quite frankly and sincerely. In addressing grown-ups the only safe medium of expression is irony.

GLEANED by R. J. S. from a Topeka church calendar: "Preaching at 8 p. m., subject 'A Voice from Hell.' Miss Holman will sing."

HERE is a happy little suggestion for traveling men, offered by S. B. T.: "When entering the dining room of a hotel, why not look searchingly about and rub hands together briskly?"

[13]

WHAT could be more frank than the framed motto in the Hotel Fortney, at Viroqua, Wis.—"There Is No Place Like Home."?

As to why hotelkeepers charge farmers less than they charge traveling men, one of our readers discovered the reason in 1899: The gadder takes a bunch of toothpicks after each meal and pouches them; the farmer takes only one, and when he is finished with it he puts it back.

IF Plato were writing to-day he would have no occasion to revise his notion of democracy—"a charming form of government, full of variety and disorder, and dispensing equality to equals and unequals alike."

THE older we grow the more impressed we are by the amount of bias in the world. Thank heaven, the only prejudices we have are religious, racial, and social prejudices. In other respects we are open to reason.

FROM the calendar of the Pike county court: "Shank vs. Shinn."
Strange all this difference should have been
'Twixt Mr. Shank and Mr. Shinn.

HOME TIES.

Sir: Discovered, in Minnesota, the country delegate who goes to bed wearing the tie his daughter tied on him before he left home, because he wouldn't know how to tie it in the morning if he took it off. J. O. C.

THEY FOUND THEM IN THE ALLEY.

Sir: A young man promised a charming young woman, as a birthday remembrance, a rose for every year she was old. After he had given the order for two dozen Killarneys, the florist said to his boy: "He's a good customer. Just put in half a dozen extra." M. C. G.

"WHEN," inquires a fair reader, apropos of our remark that the only way to improve the so-called human race is to junk it and begin over again, "when does the junking begin? Because . . ." Cawn't say when the big explosion will occur. But look for us in a neighboring constellation.

When they junk the human species
We will meet you, love, in Pisces.

THE TOONERVILLE TROLLEY.

Sir: Did you ever ride on a street car in one of those towns where no one has any place to go and all day to get there in? The conversation runs something like this between the motorman and conductor:

Conductor: "Ding ding!" (Meaning, "I'm ready whenever you are.")

Motorman: "Ding ding!" ("Well, I'm ready.")

Conductor: "Ding ding!" ("All right, you can go.")

Motorman: "Ding ding!" ("I gotcha, Steve.")

Then they go.   P. I. N.

O WILD! O STRANGE!

"That wild and strange thing, the press."—H. G. WELLS.

It's now too late, I fear, to change,
    For ever since a child
I've always been a little strange,
    And just a little wild.

I never knew the reason why,
    But now the cause I guess—
What Mr. Wells, the author, calls
    "That wild, strange thing, the press."

I've worked for every kind of pape
    In journalism's range,
And some were tame and commonplace,
    But most were wild and strange.

I ran a country paper once—
  Or, rather, it ran me;
It was the strangest, wildest thing
  That ever you did see.

Some years ago I settled down
  And thought to find a cure
By writing books and plays and sich,
  That class as litrachoor.

And for a time I lived apart,
  In abject happiness;
Yet all the while I hankered for
  That strange, wild thing, the press.

Its fatal fascination I
  Could not resist for long;
I fled the path of litrachoor,
  And once again went wrong.

I resurrected this here Col,
  By which you are beguiled.
I fear you find it strange sometimes,
  And always rather wild.

A DELEGATION of Socialists has returned from
Russia with the news that Sovietude leaves everything to be desired, that "things are worse than
in the Czarist days." Naturally. The trouble
is, the ideal is more easily achieved than retained.
The ideal existed for a few weeks in Russia. It

[17]

was at the time of the canning of Kerensky. Everybody had authority and nobody had it. Lincoln Steffens, beating his luminous wings in the void, beamed with joy. The ideal had been achieved; all government had disappeared. But this happy state could not last. The people who think such a happy state can last are the most interesting minds outside of the high brick wall which surrounds the institution.

WHEN one consults what he is pleased to call his mind, this planet seems the saddest and maddest of possible worlds. And when one walks homeward under a waning moon, through Suburbia's deserted lanes, between hedges that exhale the breath of lilac and honeysuckle, the world seems a very satisfactory half-way house on the road to the Unknown. Shall we trust our intelligence or our senses? If we follow the latter it is because we wish to, not because they are a more trustworthy guide.

ONE must agree with Mr. Yeats, that the poetic drama is for a very small audience, but we should not like to see it so restricted. For a good share of the amusement which we get out of life comes from watching the attempts to feed caviar to the general.

THE POPOCATEPETL OF APPRECIATION.

[From the Paris, Ill., News.]

For the past seven days I have been an inmate at the county jail, and through the columns of the Daily News I wish to express my thanks and appreciation to Sheriff and Mrs. McCallister and Mr. McDaniel for the kindness shown to me. I have been in jail before, here and at other places, and never found a like institution kept in such a sanitary condition. The food prepared by Mrs. McCallister was excellent. In my opinion Mr. McCallister is entitled to any office.

May Claybaugh.

A COPY of the second edition of The Ozark Harpist is received. The Harpist is Alys Hale, who sings on the flyleaf:

"Sing on, my harp,
Sing on some more and ever,
For sweet souls are breaking,
And fond hearts are aching,
Sing on some more and ever!"

WE quite agree with Mr. Masefield that great literary work requires leisure. Lack of leisure is handicapping us in the writing of a romance. We compose it while waiting for trains, while shoveling snow and coal, while riding on the L, while shaving; and we write it on the backs of envelopes, on the covering of packages, on the margins of newspapers. The best place to write a book is in jail, where Cervantes wrote Don Quixote; but we can't find time to commit a greater misdemeanor than this column, and there is no jail sentence for that. The only compensation for the literary method we are forced to adopt is that there is a great deal of "go" in it.

REPLYING to an extremely dear reader: Whenever we animadvert on the human race we include ourself. We share its imperfections, and we hope we are tinctured with its few virtues. As a race it impresses us as a flivver; we feel as you, perhaps, feel in your club when, looking over the members, you wonder how the dickens most of them got in.

PROF. PICKERING is quoted as declaring that a race of superior beings inhabits the moon. Now we are far from claiming that the inhabitants of our geoid are superior to the moon folk, or any other folk in the solar system; but the mere fact that the Moonians are able to exist in conditions peculiar to themselves does not make them superior. The whale can live under water. Is the whale, then, superior to, say, Senator Johnson? True, it can spout farther, but it is probably inferior to Mr. Johnson in reasoning power.

The man who tells you that he believes "in principles, not men," means—nothing at all. One would think that in the beginning God created a set of principles, and man was without form and void.

"Lost—Pair of trousers while shopping. Finder call Dinsmore 1869."—Minneapolis Journal.

The female of the shopping species is rougher and more ruthless than the male.

"Ancient Rome, in the height of her glory, with her lavish amusements, Olympian games," etc.—The enraptured advertiser.

The proof reader asks us if it was an eruption of Mt. Olympus that destroyed Pompeii.

GARDENS.

My lady hath a garden fair,
　　Wherein she whiles her hours:
She chides me that I do not share
　　Her rage for springing flowers.

I tell her I've a garden, too,
　　Wherein I have to toil—
The kind that Epicurus knew,
　　If not so good a soil.

And I must till my patch with care,
  And watch its daily needs;
For lacking water, sun, and air,
  The place would run to weeds.

In this the garden of the mind,
  My flowers are all too few;
Yet am I well content to find
  A modest bloom or two.

My lady hath a garden fair,
  Or will when buds are blown:
I've but a blossom here and there—
  Poor posies, but mine own.

"VERY well, here is a constructive criticism," declared Col. Roosevelt, tossing another grenade into the administration trenches. The Colonel is our favorite constructive critic. After he has finished a bit of construction it takes an hour for the dust to settle.

JUDGMENT DAY will be a complete performance for the dramatic critics. They will be able to stay for the last act.

WHY is it that when a woman takes the measurements for a screen door she thinks she has to allow a couple of inches to turn in?

"WOMAN Lights 103 Candles With One Match."

Huh! Helen, with one match, lit the topless towers of Ilium.

It may be—nay, it is—ungallant so to say, but—— Well, have you, in glancing over the beauty contest exhibits, observed a face that would launch a thousand ships? Or five hundred?

"Learn to Speak on Your Feet," advertises a university extension. We believe we could tell all we know about ours in five hundred words.

GOOD NIGHT!
[From the Omaha Bee.]

Mrs. Riley gave a retiring party in honor of her husband.

At the Hotel Dwan, in Benton Harbor, "rooms may be had en suite or connecting." Or should you prefer that they lead one into another, the management will be glad to accommodate you.

Government census blanks read on top of sheet: "Kindly fill out questions below." One of the questions is: "Can you read? Can you write? Yes or No?" This reminds a Minneapolis man of the day when he was about 15 miles from Minneapolis and read on a guide post: "15 miles to Minneapolis. If you cannot read, ask at the grocery store."

[23]

THE wave of spiritualism strikes Mr. Leacock as absurd, simply absurd. "And yet people seem to be going mad over it," he adds. What do you mean "and yet," Stephen? Don't you mean "consequently"?

A JOLIET social item mentions the engagement of Miss Lucille Muff De Line. We don't recall her contribution.

Gilded Fairy Tales.

(Revised and regilded for comprehension by the children of the very rich.)

THE BABES IN THE WOOD.

I

ONCE upon a time there dwelt in a small but very expensive cottage on the outskirts of a pine forest a gentleman with his wife and two children. It was a beautiful estate and the neighborhood was the very best. Nobody for miles around was worth less than five million dollars.

One night the gentleman tapped at his wife's boudoir, and receiving permission to enter, he said: "Pauline, I have been thinking about our children. I overheard the governess say to-day that they are really bright and interesting, and as yet unspoiled. Perhaps if they had a fair chance they might amount to something."

"Reginald," replied his wife, "you are growing morbid about those children. You will be asking to see them next." She shrugged her gleaming shoulders, and rang for the maid to let down her hair.

"Remember our own youth and shudder, Pauline," said the gentleman. "It's a shame to allow

Percival and Melisande to grow up in this atmosphere."

"Well," said the lady petulantly, "what do you suggest?"

"I think it would be wise and humane to abandon them. The butler or the chauffeur can take them into the wood and lose them and some peasant may find and adopt them, and they may grow up to be worthy citizens. At least it is worth trying."

"Do as you please," said the lady. "The children are a collaboration; they are as much yours as mine."

This conversation was overheard by little Melisande, who had stolen down from her little boudoir in her gold-flowered nightdress for a peep at her mamma, whom she had not seen for a long, long time. The poor child was dreadfully frightened, and crept upstairs weeping to her brother.

"Pooh!" said Percival, who was a brave little chap. "We shall find our way out of the wood, never fear. Give me your pearl necklace, Melisande."

The wondering child dried her eyes and fetched the necklace, and Percival stripped off the pearls and put them in the pocket of his velvet jacket. "They can't lose us, sis," said he.

In the morning the butler took the children a long, long way into the woods, pretending that he had discovered a diamond mine; and, bidding them stand in a certain place till he called, he went away and did not return. Melisande began to weep, as usual, but Percival only laughed, for he had dropped a pearl every little way as they entered the wood, and the children found their way home without the least difficulty. Their father was vexed by their cleverness, but their mamma smiled.

"It's fate, Reginald," she remarked. "They were born for the smart set, and they may as well fulfill their destinies."

"Let us try once more," said the gentleman. "Give them another chance."

When the servant called the children the next morning Percival ran to get another pearl necklace, but the jewel cellar was locked, and the best he could do was to conceal a four-pound bunch of hothouse grapes under his jacket. This time they were taken twice as far into the wood in search of the diamond mine; and alas! when the butler deserted them Percival found that the birds had eaten every grape he had dropped along the way. They were now really lost, and wandered all day without coming out anywhere, and at night

they slept on a pile of leaves, which Percival said
was much more like camping out than their summer in the Adirondacks. All next day they wandered, without seeing sign of a road or a château,
and Melisande wept bitterly.

"I am so hungry," exclaimed the poor child.
"If we only could get a few *marrons glacés* for
breakfast!"

"I could eat a few macaroons myself," said
Percival.

III

On the afternoon of the third day Percival
and Melisande came to a strange little cottage
fashioned of gingerbread, but as the children had
never tasted anything so common as gingerbread
they did not recognize it. However, the cottage
felt soft and looked pretty enough to eat, so Percival bit off a piece of the roof and declared it
was fine. Melisande helped herself to the doorknob, and the children might have eaten half the
cottage had not a witch who lived in it come out
and frightened them away. The children ran as
fast as their legs could work, for the witch looked
exactly like their governess, who tried to make
them learn to spell and do other disagreeable
tasks.

Presently they came out on a road and saw a
big red automobile belonging to nobody in par-

ticular. It was the most beautiful car imaginable. The hubs were set with pigeon blood rubies and the spokes with brilliants; the tires were set with garnets to prevent skidding, and the hood was inlaid with diamonds and emeralds. Even Percival and Melisande were impressed. One door stood invitingly open and the children sprang into the machine. They were accustomed to helping themselves to everything that took their fancy; they had inherited the instinct.

Percival turned on the gas. "Hang on to your hair, sis!" he cried, and he burnt up the road all the way home, capsizing the outfit in front of the mansion and wrecking the automobile.

Their mamma came slowly down the veranda steps with a strange gentleman by her side. "These are the children, Edward," she said, picking them up, uninjured by the spill. "Children, this is your new papa."

The gentleman shook hands with them very pleasantly and said he hoped that he should be their papa long enough to get really acquainted with them. At which remark the lady smiled and tapped him with her fan.

And they lived happily, after their fashion, ever afterward.

LITTLE RED RIDING-HOOD.

I

Once upon a time there was a little girl who was the prettiest creature imaginable. Her mother was excessively fond of her, and saw her as frequently as possible, sometimes as often as once a month. Her grandmother, who doted on her even more, had made for her in Paris a little red riding hood of velvet embroidered with pearl passementerie, which became the child so well that everybody in her set called her Little Red Riding-Hood.

One day her mother said to her: "Go, my dear, and see how your grandmother does, for I hear she has been ill with indigestion. Carry her this filet and this little pot of foie gras."

The grandmother lived in a secluded and exclusive part of the village, in a marble cottage situated in the midst of a wooded park. Little Red Riding-Hood got out of the motor when she came to the park, telling the chauffeur she would walk the rest of the way. She hardly passed the hedge when she met a Wolf.

"Whither are you going?" he asked, looking wistfully at her.

"I am going to see my grandmother, and carry her a filet and a little pot of foie gras from my mamma."

"Well," said the Wolf, "I'll go see her, too. I'll go this way and you go that, and we shall see who will be there first."

The Wolf ran off as fast as he could, and was first at the door of the marble cottage. The butler informed him that Madame was not at home, but he sprang through the door, knocking the servant over, and ran upstairs to Madame's boudoir.

"Who's there?" asked the grandmother, when the Wolf tapped at the door.

"Your grandchild, Little Red Riding-Hood," replied the Wolf, counterfeiting the child's voice, "who has brought you a filet and a little pot of foie gras."

II

The good grandmother, who had eaten nothing for two days except a mallard, with a pint of champagne, cried out hungrily, "Come in, my dear."

The Wolf ran in, and, falling upon the old lady, ate her up in a hurry, for he had not tasted food for a whole week. He then got into the bed, and presently Little Red Riding-Hood tapped at the door.

The Wolf pitched his voice as high and unpleasant as he could, and called out, "What is it, Hawkins?"

[31]

"It isn't Hawkins," replied Little Red Riding-Hood. "It is your grandchild, who has brought you a filet and a little pot of foie gras."

"Come in, my dear," responded the Wolf. And when the child entered he said: "Put the filet and the little pot of foie gras on the gold tabouret, and come and lie down with me."

Little Red Riding-Hood did not think it good form to go to bed so very, very late in the morning, but as she expected to inherit her grandmother's millions she obediently took off her gold-flowered frock, and her pretty silk petticoat, and her dear little diamond stomacher, and got into bed, where, amazed at the change for the better in her grandmother's appearance, she said to her:

"Grandmother, how thin your arms have got!"

"I have been dieting, my dear."

"Grandmother, how thin your legs have got!"

"The doctor makes me walk every day."

"Grandmother, how quiet you are!"

"This isn't a symphony concert hall, my dear."

"Grandmother, what has become of your diamond-filled teeth?"

"These will do, my dear."

And saying these words the wicked Wolf fell upon Little Red Riding-Hood and ate her all up.

JACK AND THE BEANSTALK.

I

Once upon a time there was a very wealthy widow who lived in a marble cottage approached by a driveway of the same stone, bordered with rhododendrons. She had an only son, Jack—a giddy, thoughtless boy, but very kindhearted, as many a hard-working chorus girl had reason to remember. Jack was an idle fellow, whose single accomplishment was driving an automobile, in which he displayed remarkable skill and recklessness; there was hardly a day he did not run over something or somebody. One day he bumped a very heavy workingman, whose remains messed up the car so badly that Jack's mother lost patience with him. "My dear," she said, "why don't you put your skill and energy to some use? If only you would slay the giant Ennui, who ravages our country, you would be as great a hero in our set as St. George of England was in his."

Jack laughed. "Let him but get in the way of my car," said he, "and I'll knock him into the middle of next month."

The boy set out gaily for the garage, to have the motor repaired, and on the way he met a green-goods grocer who displayed a handful of beautiful red, white, and blue beans. Jack stopped to look at what he supposed was a new kind of poker chip, and the man persuaded the silly youth to exchange the automobile for the beans.

When he brought home the "chips" his mother laughed loudly. "You are just like your father; he didn't know beans, either," she said. "Dig a hole in the tennis court, Jack, and plant your poker chips, and see what will happen."

Jack did as he was told to do, and the next morning he went out to see whether anything had happened. What was his amazement to find that a mass of twisted stalks had grown out of his jackpot and climbed till they covered the high cliff back of the tennis court, disappearing above it.

II

Jack came of a family of climbers. His mother had climbed into society and was still climbing. The funny thing about climbers is that they never deceive anybody; every one knows just what they are up to. As Jack had inherited the climbing passion he began without hesitation to ascend the beanstalk, and when he reached the top he was as tired as if he had spent the day laying bricks or selling goods behind a counter; but he perked up when he beheld a fairy in pink tights who looked very much like a coryphée in the first row of "The Girly Girl."

"Is this a roof garden?" asked Jack, looking about him curiously.

"No, kid," replied the Fairy, tapping him playfully with her spear. "You are in the Land of Pleasure, and in yonder castle lives a horrid Giant called Ennui, who bores everybody he catches to death."

Jack put on a brave face and lighted a cigarette. "Has he ever caught you, little one?" he asked.

"No," she laughed, "but I'm knocking wood. Fairies don't get bored until they grow old, or at least middle-aged."

"It's a wonder," said Jack, "that the Giant doesn't bore himself to death some day."

"He might," said the Fairy, "if it were not for his wonderful talking harp, which keeps harping upon Socialism, and the single tax, and the rights of labor, and a lot of other mush; but you see it keeps Ennui stirred up, so that he is never bored entirely stiff."

"Well," said Jack, "me for that harp, if I die for it!" And thanking Polly Twinkletoes for her information, and promising to buy her a supper when he got his next allowance, he sauntered toward the castle. As he paused before the great gate it was opened suddenly by a most unpleasant looking giantess.

"Ho! ho!" she cried, seizing Jack by the arm, "you're the young scamp who sold me that lightning cleaner last week. I'll just keep you till

you take the spots out of my husband's Sunday
pants. If you don't, he'll knock the spots out
of *you!*"

While the Giantess spoke she dragged Jack
into the castle. "Into this wardrobe," said she;
"and mind you don't make the smallest noise, or
my man will wring your neck. He takes a nap
after dinner, and then you'll have a chance to
demonstrate that grease-eradicator you sold me
last week."

The wardrobe was as big as Jack's yacht, and
the key-hole as big as a barrel, so the boy could
see everything that took place without. Presently the castle was shaken as if by an earthquake,
and a great voice roared: "Wife! wife! I smell
gasoline!"

Jack trembled, remembering that in tinkering
around his car that morning he had spilled gas
on his clothes.

"Be quiet!" replied the Giantess. "It's only
the lightning-cleaner which that scamp of a ped-
dler sold me the other day."

The Giant ate a couple of sheep; then, pushing
his plate away, he called for his talking harp.
And while he smoked, the harp rattled off a long
string of stuff about the equal liability of all men
to labor, the abolition of the right of inheritance,
and kindred things. Jack resolved that when he

[36]

got hold of the harp he would serve it at a formal dinner, under a great silver cover. What a sensation it would cause among his guests when it began to sing its little song about the abolition of the right of inheritance!

In a short time the Giant fell asleep, for the harp, like many reformers, became wearisome through exaggeration of statement. Jack slipped from the wardrobe, seized the harp, and ran out of the castle.

"Master! Master!" cried the music-maker. "Wake up! We are betrayed!"

Glancing back, Jack saw the Giant striding after him, and gave himself up for lost; but at that moment he heard his name called, and he saw the Fairy, Polly Twinkletoes, beckoning to him from a taxicab. Jack sprang into the machine and they reached the beanstalk a hundred yards ahead of the giant. Down the stalk they slipped and dropped, the Giant lumbering after. Once at the bottom, Jack ran to the garage and got out his man-killer, and when the Giant reached ground he was knocked, as Jack had promised, into the middle of the proximate month.

Our hero married the Fairy, much against his mother's wishes; she knew her son all too well, and she felt certain that she should soon come to know Polly as well, and as unfavorably. Things turned out no better than she had expected.

[37]

After a month of incompatibility, and worse, Polly consented to a divorce in consideration of one hundred thousand dollars, and they all lived happily ever afterward.

"FAY CE QUE VOULDRAS."

*D*O *what thou wilt.* Long known to fame
    That ancient motto of Thélème.
  To this our abbey hither bring,
  Wisdom or wit, thine offering,
Or low or lofty be thine aim.

Here is no virtue in a name,
But all are free to play the game.
  Here, welcome as the flow'rs of Spring,
      Do what thou wilt.

Each in these halls a place may claim,
And is, if sad, alone to blame.
  Kick up thy heels and dance and sing—
  To any wild conceit give wing—
Be fool or sage, 'tis all the same—
      Do what thou wilt.

THAT was an amusing tale of the man who complained of injuries resulting from a loaded seegar. He knew when he smoked it that it was a trick weed, and knew that it would explode, but he "didn't know when." He reminds us very strongly of a parlor bolshevist.

[39]

"MAN," as they sing in "Princess Ida," "is nature's sole mistake." And he never appears more of a rummy than when some woman kills herself for him, in his embarrassed presence. His first thought is always of himself.

A HISTORY exam in a public school contains this delightful information: "Patrick Henry said, 'I rejoice that I have but one country to live for.'"

TIME travels in divers paces with divers persons. There are some who, like a certain capable rounder, lately departed, have time to manage a large business, maintain two or more domestic establishments, razz, jazz, get drunk, and fight; while others of us cannot find time in the four and twenty hours to do half the things we wish to achieve. Although your orator has nothing to do but "write a few headlines and go home," as Old Bill Byrne says, night overtakes him with half his chores undone. Time gallops withal.

"THEY know what they like."
There are exceptions. The author of "Set Down in Malice" mentions a number, the most conspicuous being Ernest Newman. And we recall an exception, Mr. Jimmie Whittaker, merriest of critics, who was so far from knowing what he liked that he adopted the plan, in considering the Symphony concerts, of praising the even num-

bers one week and damning the even numbers the following week.

LIKE Ernest Newman, we shall never again hear the Chopin Funeral March without being reminded of Mr. Sidgwick's summary: "Most funeral marches seem to cheer up in the middle and become gloomy again. I suppose the idea is, (1) the poor old boy's dead; (2) well, after all, he's probably gone to heaven; (3) still, anyhow, the poor old boy's dead."

OUR readers, we swear, know everything. One of them writes from La Crosse that Debussy's "Canope" has nothing to do with the planet Canopus, but refers to the ancient Egyptian city of that name. Mebbe so (we should like proof of it), but what of it?—as Nero remarked when they told him Rome was afire. The Debussy music does as well for the star as for the city. It is ethereal, far away, and it leaves off in midair. There is a passage in "Orpheus and Eurydice" which is wedded to words expressing sorrow; but, as has been pointed out, the music would go as well or better with words expressing joy.

"LINCOLN," observed Old Bill Byrne, inserting a meditative pencil in the grinder, "said you can fool all the people some of the time. But that

[41]

was in the sixties, before the Colyum had developed a bunch of lynx-eyed, trigger-brained, hawk-swooping, owl-pouncing fans that nobody can fool for a holy minute."

FISHING for errors in a proof-room is like fishing for trout: the big ones always get away. Or, as Old Bill Byrne puts it, while you're fishing for a minnow a whale comes up and bites you in the leg.

WHENE'ER we take our walks abroad we meet acquaintances who view with alarm the immediate future of the self-styled human race; but we find ourself unable to share their apprehension. We do not worry about lead, or iron, or any other element. And human nature is elemental. You can flatten it, as in Russia; you can bend, and twist, and pound it into various forms, but you cannot decompose it. And so the "new order," while perhaps an improvement on the old, will not be so very different. Britannia will go on ruling the waves, and Columbia, not Utopia, will be the gem of the ocean.

"WOMAN'S Club Will Hear Dr. Ng Poon Chew."—Minneapolis News.
We believe this is a libel on Dr. Poon.

THE Greek drachma is reported to be in a bad way. Perhaps a Drachma League could uplift it and tide it over the crisis.

THE DELIRIOUS CRITIC.

[From the Sheridan, Wyo., Enterprise.]

Replete with fine etherially beautiful melody and graceful embellishments, it represents Mozart at his best, expressing in a form as clear and finely finished as a delicate ivory carving that mood of restful, sunny, impersonal optimism which is the essence of most of his musical creations. It is like some finely wrought Greek idyl, the apotheosis of the pastoral, perfect in detail, without apparent effort, gently, tenderly emotional, without a trace of passionate intensity or restless agitation, innocent and depending, as a mere babe. It is the mood of a bright, cloudless day on the upland pastures, where happy shepherds watch their peaceful flocks, untroubled by the storm and stress of our modern life, a mood so foreign to the hearts and environment of most present day human beings, that it is rarely understood by player or hearer, and still more rarely enjoyed. It seems flat and insipid as tepid water to the fevered lips of the young passion-driven, ambition-goaded soul in its first stormy period of struggle and achievement; but later, it is welcomed as the answer to that inarticulate, but ever

[43]

increasingly frequent, sign for peace and tranquil beauty.

SOMEWHERE IN THE MICHIGAN WOODS.

Sir: Last night I disturbed the family catawollapus—née Irish—with, "Are you asleep, Maggie?" "Yis, sor." "Too bad, Maggie; the northern lights are out, and you ought to see them." "I'm sorry, sor, but I'm sure I filled them all this morning." What I intended to say was that I have taken the liberty of christening a perfectly good he-pointer pup Jet Wimp. Hope it is not lese majesté against the revered president of the Immortals.

Salvilinus Fontanalis.

A Sheboygan merchant announces a display of "what Dame Nature has decreed women shall wear this fall and winter."

In considering additions to the Academy of Immortals shall Anna Quaintance be forgot? She lives in Springfield.

A box-office man has won the politeness prize. Topsy-turvy world, did you say?

We lamp by the rural correspondence that Mrs. Alfred Snow of Chili, Wis., is on her way to Bismarck, N. D. It is suggested that she detour to Hot Springs and warm up a bit.

BLAKE COMES BACK.

Little Ford, who made thee?
Dost thou know who made thee,
Gave thee gas and bade thee speed
By the stream and o'er the mead;
Gave thee cushions hard and tight,
Bumpy tires small and white;
Gave thee such a raucous voice,
Making all the deaf rejoice?
Little Ford, who made thee?
Dost thou know who made thee?

Little Ford, I'll tell thee,
Little Ford, I'll tell thee.
He is callèd by thy name,
Henry Ford, the very same.
He is meek and he is mild,
Is pacific as a child.
He a child and thou a Ford,
You are callèd the same word.
Little Ford, God bless thee!
Little Ford, God bless thee!

B. L.

EVERYBODY CAME IN A FORD.

[From the Milwaukee Sentinel.]

Miss Evelyn Shallow, daughter of Mr. and Mrs. Peter Shallow, and Raymond Bridger, both of Little River, were married recently at Oconto.

[45]

CONSIDERING the pictorial advertisements, A. B. Walkley finds that that triumphant figure of the active, bustling world, the business man, divides his day somewhat as follows: He begins with his toilet, which seems to center in or near his chin, which is prominent, square, firm, and smooth; even the rich, velvety lather cannot disguise it. The business man collects safety razors; he collects collars, too. He seems to be in the habit of calling in his friends to see how perfectly his shirt fits at the neck. Once dressed, he goes to his office and is to be found at an enormous desk bristling with patent devices, pleasantly gossiping with another business man. You next find him in evening dress at the dinner table, beaming at the waiter who has brought him his favorite sauce. Lastly you have a glimpse of him in pajamas, discoursing with several other business men in pajamas, all sitting cross-legged and smoking enormous cigars. This is the end of a perfect business day.

MR. KIPLING has obtained an injunction and damages because a medicine company used a stanza of his "If" to boost its pills. While we do not think much of the verses, we are glad the public is reminded that the little things which a poet dashes off are as much private property as a bottle of pills or a washing machine.

ANIMALS in a new Noah's Ark are made correctly to the scale designed by a London artist who studies the beasts in the Zoo. Would you buy such an ark for a child? Neither would we.

SOCIAL nuances are indicated by a farmer not far from Chicago in his use of table coverings, as follows: For the family, oil cloth; for the school teacher, turkey red; for the piano tuner, white damask.

SHE SAT APART.

Sir: We were talking across the aisle. Presently the girl who sat alone leaned over and said: "You and the lady take this seat. I'm not together."   A. H. H. A.

THE G. P. P.

Sir: What is the gadder's pet peeve? Mine is to be aroused by the hotel maid who jiggles the doorknob at 8 a.m., when the little indicator shows the room is still locked from the inside. It happened to me to-day at the Blackhawk in Davenport.   W. S.

BEG YOUR PARDON.

W. S. writes, after a long session with his boss, that the recent announcement he was disturbed at 8 o'clock by the rattling of his hotel door was a typographical error committed in this office (sic), the hour as stated by him really having been 6.30 a.m.

THE manager of the Hotel Pomeroy, Barbados, W. I., warns: "No cigarettes or cocktails served to married ladies without husband's consent."

IT is years since we read "John Halifax, Gentleman," but we must dust off the volume. The Japanese translation has a row of asterisks and the editor's explanation: "At this point he asked her to marry him."

GADDERS have many grievances, and one of them is the small-town grapefruit. One traveler offers the stopper of a silver flask for an authentic instance of a grapefruit served without half of the tough interior thrown in for good measure.

IF Jedge Landis has time to attend to another job, a great many people would like to see him take hold of the Senate and establish in it the confidence of the public. It would be a tougher job than baseball reorganization, but it is thought he could swing it.

YES?

You may fancy it is easy,
  When the world is fighting drunk,
To compile a colyum wheezy

With a lot of airy junk—
To maintain a mental quiet
  And a philosophic ca'm,
And to give, amid the riot,
  Not a dam.

You may think it is no trick to
  Can the topic militaire,
And determinedly stick to
  Jape and jingle light as air—
To be pertly paragraphic
  And to jollity inclined,
In an evenly seraphic
  State of mind.

When our anger justified is,
  And the nation's on the brink;
When Herr Dernburg—durn his hide!—is
  To be chased across the drink;
When the cabinet is meeting,
  And the ultimatums fly,
And the tom-toms are a-beating
  A defy;

When it's raining gall and bitters—
  You may think it is a pipe
To erect a Tower of Titters
  With a lot of lines o' type,
To be whimsical and wheezy,
  Full of { quip and quirk and quiz.
           { quibbles queer and quaint.
Do you fancy *that* is easy?
  Well—it { is.
          { ain't.

[49]

THE dissolution of Farmer Pierson, of Princeton, Ill., from rough-on-rats administered, it is charged, by his wife and her gentleman friend, is a murder case that reminds us of New England, where that variety of triangle reaches stages of grewsomeness surpassed only by "The Love of Three Kings." How often, in our delirious reporter days, did we journey to some remote village in Vermont or New Hampshire, to inquire into the passing of an honest agriculturist whose wife, assisted by the hired man, had spiced his biscuits with arsenic or strychnine.

ON the menu of the Woman's City Club: "Scrambled Brains." Do you wonder, my dear?

WE quite understand that if Mr. Moiseiwitsch is to establish himself with the public he must play old stuff, even such dreadful things as the Mozart-Liszt "Don Giovanni." It is with Chopin valses and Liszt rhapsodies that a pianist plays an audience into a hall, but he should put on some stuff to play the audience out with. Under this arrangement those of us who have heard Chopin's Fantasie as often as we can endure may come late, while those who do not "understand" Debussy, Albeniz, and other moderns may leave early. The old stuff is just as good to-day as it was twenty years ago, but some of us ancients have got past that stage of musical development.

THE MOST EMBARRASSING MOMENT.

Sir: This story was related to me by Modeste Mignon, who hesitates to give it to the "Embarrassing Moments" editor:

"Going down Michigan avenue one windy day, I stopped to fix my stocking, which had come unfastened. Just as my hands were both engaged a gust of wind lifted one of my hair tabs and exposed almost the whole of my left ear. I was never so embarrassed in my life."

BALLYMOONEY.

THE ENRAPTURED REPORTER.
[From the White Salmon Enterprise.]

The bridal couple stood under festoons of Washington holly, and in front of a circling hedge of flowering plants, whose delicate pink blossoms gave out a faint echo of the keynote of the bride's ensemble.

EVERYTHING CONSIDERED, THE COMMA IS THE MOST USEFUL MARK OF PUNCTUATION.
[From the El Paso Journal.]

Prof. Bone, head of the rural school department of the Normal University, gave an address to the parents and teachers of Eureka, Saturday evening.

GALESBURG's Hotel Custer has sprung a new one on the gadders. Bub reports that, instead of the conventional "Clerk on Duty, Mr. Rae," the card reads: "Greeter, Rudie Hawks."

A COMMUNICATION to La Follette's Magazine is signed by W.E.T.S. Nurse, N. Y. City. What is the "S" for?

BETTER LATE THAN NEVER.
[From the Walsh County, N. D., Record.]

A quiet wedding occurred Friday, when Francis A. Tardy of Bemidji, Minn., was united in marriage to Miss Leeva Ness.

THE ENRAPTURED REPORTER; OR, IT INDEED WAS.
[From the St. Andrew's Bay, Fla., News.]

Mrs. Paddock, Mrs. Russell, Mrs. Templeton, and Mrs. Cottingham, all of whom are visiting Mrs. Turesdel, the hostess of Monday's picnic, were keenly appreciative of such bits of beauty as the day revealed. Florida, herself a hostess of lavish hospitality, seemed to be more radiant, and when night came and the boat pulled her way out into the bay, still another surprise awaited the northerners. In the wake of the boat shimmered a thousand, yea, a million jewels. The little waves crested with opals and pearls. The weirdly beautiful phenomena filled the visitors with delighted wonder as they leaned over the water and watched the flashing colors born of the night. As the lights of our city hove into view, the voice of Mrs. Templeton, a voice marvelously sweet, sang "The End of a Perfect Day," as indeed it was.

A "MASQUERADE pie supper" was given in Paris, Ill., last week. The kind of pie used is not mentioned, but it must have been either cranberry or sweet potato.

CONTRETEMPS IN WYOMING SOCIETY.
[From the Sheridan Post.]

No finer dressed party of men and women ever assembled together in this city than those who took part in the ball given by the bachelors of Sheridan to their married friends. Many of the costumes deserve mention, but the Post man is not capable of describing them properly. The supper and refreshments were of the kind that all appreciated, and was served at just the right time by obliging waiters, who seemed to enter into the spirit of the times and make every one feel satisfied. Only one deplorable thing transpired at the dance, and it was nobody's fault. Dr. Newell had the misfortune to lean too far forward when bowing to a lady and tear his pants across the

[53]

seams. He had filled his program, and had a beautiful partner for each number, but he had to back off and sit down.

MERCIFULLY SEPARATED.

Sir: A fellow-gadder is sitting opposite me at this writing table. It seems that some old friend of his in Texas, out of work, funds, and food, has written him for aid, and he is replying: "Glad you're so far away, so we sha'n't see each other starve to death."   SIM NIC.

FREEDOM shrieked when Venizelos fell. But Freedom has grown old and hysterical, and shrieks on very little occasion.

THE attitude of the Greeks toward "that fine democrat Venizelos" reminds our learned contemporary the Journal of the explanation given by the ancient Athenian who voted against Aristides: he was tired of hearing him called "the Just." It is an entirely human sentiment, one of the few that justify the term "human race." It swept away Woodrow the Idealist, and all the other issues that the parties set up. If it were not for the saturation point, the race would be in danger of becoming inhuman.

THE allies quarreled among themselves during the war, and have been quarreling ever since. A

[54]

world war and a world peace are much too big jobs for any set of human heads.

ACADEMY NOTES.

Sir: If there is a school of expression connected with the Academy I nominate for head of it Elizabeth Letzkuss, principal of the Greene school, Chicago. CALCITROSUS.

MEMBERS of the Academy will be pleased to know that their fellow-Immortal, Mr. Gus Wog, was elected in North Dakota.

WE regret to learn that one of our Immortals, Mr. Tinder Tweed, of Harlan, Ky., has been indicted for shooting on the highway.

TO MARY GARDEN—WITH A POSTSCRIPT.

So wonderful your art, if you preferred
Drayma to opry, you'd be all the mustard;
For you (ecstatic pressmen have averred)
Have Sarah Bernhardt larruped to a custard.

So marvelous your voice, too, if you cared
With turns and trills and tra-la-las to dazzle,
You'd have (enraptured critics have declared)
All other singers beaten to a frazzle.

So eloquent your legs, were it your whim
To caper nimbly in a classic measure,
Terpsichore (entranced reviewers hymn)
Would swoon upon her lyre for very pleasure.

If there be aught you *cannot* do, 'twould seem
The world has yet that something to discover.
One has to hand it to you. You're a scream.
And 'tis a joy to watch you put it over.

Postscriptum.

If there be any test you can't survive,
The present test will mean your crucifying;
But I am laying odds of eight to five
That you'll come thro' with all your colors flying.

IT IS chiefly a matter of temperament. And more impudence and assurance is required to crack a safe or burglarize a dwelling than to cancel a shipment of goods in order to avoid a loss; but one is as honest a deed as the other. Or it would be better to say that one is as poor policy as the other. For it is not claimed that man is an honest animal; it is merely agreed that honesty profits him most in the long run.

ACADEMY JOTTINGS.

J. P. W.: "I present Roley Akers of Boone, Ia., as director of the back-to-the-farm movement."

C. M. V.: "For librarian to the Immortals I nominate Mrs. Bessie Hermann Twaddle, who has resigned a similar position in Tulare county, California."

THIS world cannot be operated on a sentimental basis. The experiment has been made on a small scale, and it has always failed; on a large scale it would only fail more magnificently. People who are naturally kind of heart, and of less than average selfishness, wish that the impossible might be compassed, but, unless they are half-witted, or are paid agitators, they recognize that the impossible is well named. Self-interest is the core of human nature, and before that core could be appreciably modified, if ever, the supply of heat from the sun would be so reduced that the noblest enthusiasm would be chilled. The utmost achievable in this sad world is an enlightened self-interest. This we expect of the United States when the peace makers gather. Anything more selfish would be a reproach to our professed principles. Anything less selfish would be a reproach to our intelligence.

I SHOT AN ARROW INTO THE AIR, IT WENT RIGHT THROUGH MISS BURROUGHS' HAIR.

[From the Dallas Bulletin.]

We quote Miss Burroughs: "I don't think B. L. T. is so good any more—it takes an intelligent person to comprehend his meaning half the time."

[57]

THE world is running short of carbonic acid, the British Association is told by Prof. Petrie. "The decomposition of a few more inches of silicates over the globe will exhaust the minute fraction of carbonic acid that still remains, and life will then become impossible." But cheer up. The Boston Herald assures us that "there is no immediate cause of alarm." Nevertheless we are disturbed. We had figured on the sun growing cold, but if we are to run out of carbonic acid before the sun winds up its affairs, a little worry will not be amiss. However, everybody will be crazy as a hatter before long, so what does it matter? Ten years ago Forbes Winslow wrote, after studying the human race and the lunacy statistics of a century: "I have no hesitation in stating that the human race has degenerated and is still progressing in a downward direction. We are gradually approaching, with the decadence of youth, a near proximity to a nation of madmen."

AS JOYCE KILMER MIGHT HAVE SAID.

[Kit Morley in the New York Evening Post.]

"The Chicago Tribune owns forests of pulp wood."
—Full-page advt.

I think that I shall never see
Aught lovely as a pulpwood tree.

A tree that grows through sunny noons
To furnish sporting page cartoons.

A tree whose fibre and whose pith
Will soon be Gumps by Sidney Smith,

And make to smile and eke *ha ha!* go
The genial people of Chicago.

A tree whose grace, toward heaven rising,
Men macerate for advertising—

A tree that lifts her arms and laughs
To be made into paragraphs. . . .

How enviable is that tree
That's growing pulp for B. L. T.

"REMAKE the World" is a large order—too
large for statesmen. Two lovers underneath the
Bough may remake the world, remold it nearer
to the heart's desire—or come as near to it as
possible; but not a gathering of political gray-
beards. For better or worse the world is made;
all we can do is modify it here and there.

THE SECOND POST

[A Swedish lady seeks congenial employment.]

Madam: A few days ago I were happy
enough to meet Mrs. J. Hansley and she told me
that you migh possible want to engauge a lady to
work for you. I am swede, in prime of like, in
superb health, queite of habits, and can handle a
ordinary house. I can give references as to char-

acktar. If you want me would you kindly write and state wadges. Or if you don't, would you do a stranger a favour and put me in thuch wit any friend that want help. I hold a very good situation in a way, but I am made to eat in the kitchen and made to feel in every way that I am a inferior. I dont like that. I dont want a situation of that kind. They are kind to me most sertainly in a way, but as I jused to be kind to my favorite saddle horse. I dont want that kind of soft soap. Yours very respecktfully, etc.

A WISCONSIN PARABLE.
[From the Fort Atkinson Union.]

A friend asks us why we keep on pounding La Follette. He says there is no use pounding away at a man after he's dead. Maybe we are like the man who was whaling a dead dog that had killed his sheep. "What are you whaling that cur for?" said a neighbor. "There is no use in that; he's dead." "Well," said the man, "I'll learn him, damn him, that there is punishment after death."

ANOTHER way to impress upon the world the fact that you have lived in it is to scratch matches on walls and woodwork. A banged door leaves no record except in the ear processes of the persons sitting near the door, whereas match scratches are creative work.

> Lives of such men all remind us
>   We can make our lives sublime,
> And, departing, leave behind us
>   Match-marks on the walls of time.

HE SHOULD.

Sir: Mr. Treetop, 6 feet 2 inches, is a porter at the St. Nicholas Hotel, Decatur. Would he add anything to the landscape gardening surrounding the Academy of Immortals?

W. N. C.

WHY THE EDITOR BEAT IT.
[From the Marengo Republican-News.]

Baptist Church, 7:30 p. m.—Popular evening service. Subject, "Fools and Idiots." A large number are expected.

SPEAKING again of "experience essential but not necessary," it was a gadder who observed to a fellow traveler in the smoker: 'It is not only customary, but we have been doing it right along."

"EVEN now," remarks an editorial colleague, "the person who says 'It is I' is conscious of a precise effort which exaggerates the ego." No such effort is made by one of our copyreaders, who never changes 'who' or 'whom' in a piece of telegraph copy; because, says he, "I never know which is right."

HERE IT IS AGAIN.

[From the classified ads.]

Saleslady, attractive, energetic, ambitious hustler. Selling experience essential but not necessary. Fred'k H. Bartlett & Co.

Her attractiveness, perchance, is also essential but not necessary.

WE see by the lith'ry notes that Vance Thompson has published another book. Probably we told you about the farmer in Queechee at whose house Vance boarded one summer. "He told me he was going to do a lot of writing," said the h. h. s. of t. to us, "and got me to hitch up and drive over to Pittsfield and buy him a quart bottle of ink. And dinged if he didn't give me the bottle, unopened, when he went back to town in the fall."

AFTER READING HARVEY'S WEEKLY.

I love Colonel Harvey,
His stuff is so warm,
And if you don't bite him
He'll do you no harm.

[62]

I'll sit by the fire
And feed him raw meat,
And Harvey will roar me
Clear off'n my feet.

THE Nobel prize for the best split infinitive has been awarded to the framer of the new administrative code of the state of Washington, which contains this:

"To, in case of an emergency requiring expenditures in excess of the amount appropriated by the legislature for any institution of the state, state officer, or department of the state government, and upon the written request of the governing authorities of the institution, the state officer, or the head of the department, and in case the board by a majority vote of all its members determines that the public interest requires it, issue a permit in writing," etc.

" 'WHEN this art reaches so high a standard the Post deems it a duty to publicly commend it.' —Edward A. Grozier, Editor and Publisher the Boston Post."

But ought a Bostonian to split his infinitives in public? It doesn't seem decent.

EVERY now and then a suburban train falls to pieces, and the trainmen wonder why. "What do you know about that?" they say. "It was as

[63]

good as new this morning." It never occurs to them that the slow but sure weakening of the rolling stock is due to Rule 7 in the "Instructions to Trainmen," which requires conductors and brakemen to close coach doors as violently as possible. Although not required to, many passengers imitate the trainmen. With them it is a desire to make a noise in the world. If a man cannot attract attention in the arts and the professions, a sure way is to bang doors behind him.

DOXOLOGY.

Praise Hearst, from whom all blessings flow!
Praise Hearst, who runs things here below.
Praise them who make him manifest—
Praise Andy L. and all the rest.

Praise Hearst because the world is round,
Because the seas with salt abound,
Because the water's always wet,
And constellations rise and set.

Praise Hearst because the grass is green,
And pleasant flow'rs in spring are seen;
Praise him for morning, night and noon.
Praise him for stars and sun and moon.

Praise Hearst, our nation's aim and end,
Humanity's unselfish friend;
And who remains, for all our debt,
A modest sweet white violet.

[64]

WE like Schubert's Unfinished Symphony, Kubla Khan, and many other unfinished things, but we have always let unfinished novels alone— unless you consider unfinished the yarn that "Q" finished for Stevenson. And so we are unable to appreciate the periodical eruptions of excitement over "The Mystery of Edwin Drood." Were we to read it, we dessay we should be as nutty as the Dickens fans.

MR. BASSO, second violin in the Minneapolis Orchestra, would seem to have missed his vocation by a few seats.

MY DEAR, YOU SHOULD HAVE SEEN FRED!
[From the Milwaukee Sentinel.]
In this one, the orchestra became a troupe of gayly appareled ballerinas, whirling in splendid abandon, with Mr. Stock as première.

ONE lamps by the advertisements that the Fokines are to dance Beethoven's "Moonshine" sonata. The hootch-kootch, as it were.

OFT IN THE STILLY WISCONSIN NIGHT.

Sir: California may have the most sunshine, but I'll bet Wisconsin has the most moonshine.
                                                        E. C. M.

DID ever a presidential candidate say a few kind words for art and literature, intimate the part they play in the civilizing of a nation, and promise to further them by all means in his power, that the people should not sink deeper into the quagmire of materialism? Probably not.

"HERCULES, when only a baby, strangled two servants," according to a bright history student. Nobody thought much about it in those days, as there were plenty to be had.

ABSOLUTE zero in entertainment has been achieved. A young woman recited or declaimed the imperishable Eighteenth Amendment in an Evanston church.

WITH Jedge Landis at the head of grand baseball and Mary Garden at the head of grand opera, the future of the greatest outdoor and indoor sports is temporarily assured.

ROME toddled before its fall.

The Delectable River.

Stibbs the Grocer zigzagged like a dragon-fly about his crowded store. Within the hour the supplies for our woodland cruise were packed in boxes and tagged, and ready for transportation. It was a brisk transaction; for Stibbs it was only one incident in a busy day. Outside the trolley clanged, and a Saturday crowd footed the main street of the Canadian city by the falls of the Saint Mary. It was hard to realize that solitude and a primal hush were only a few hours away.

I contrasted the activity in the store of Stibbs with the drowse that hung over another shop in the North Country where, in earlier years, I used to buy my supplies. Doctor Mayhew kept the shop, which flourished until a pushing Scandinavian set up a more pretentious establishment; after which the Doctor's shop faded away like the grin of Puss of Cheshire. One could not buy groceries of the Doctor in a hurry; one had no wish to. I always allowed the forenoon, as there was much foreign gossip to exchange between items, and the world's doings to be discussed. The Doctor was interested in the remotest subjects. The pestilences of the Orient and the possibility of their spreading to our shores, and eventually to the North Country, gave him much

[67]

concern; the court life at St. James's and the politics of Persia absorbed him;—local matters interested him not at all.

"Ten pounds of flour?" . . . The Doctor would pause, scoop in hand; then, abruptly reminded of a bit of unfinished business at the warehouse, he would leave the flour trembling in the balance and shuffle off, while I perched on the counter and swung my heels, and discussed packs with Ted Wakeland, another pioneer, who, spitting vigorously, averred that packing grub through the brush was all right for an Indian, but no fit task for a white man. Through the open door I could see the gentle swells of the Big Water washing along the crescent of the beach and heaping the sand in curious little crescent ridges. The sun beat hotly on the board walk. There were faint sounds in the distance, from the Indian village up the shore and the fishing community across the bay. Life in this parish of the Northland drifted by like the fleece of summer's sky.

"And three pounds of rice?"

The Doctor was back at the scales, and the weighing proceeded in leisurely and dignified fashion. Haste, truly, were unseemly. But at last the supplies were stowed in the brown pack, there were handshakings all round, and a word of advice from old heads, and I marched away with a singing heart.

Outfitting in the Doctor's shop was an event, a ceremonial, a thing to be housed in memory along with camps and trails.

II.—THE RIVER.

He who has known many rivers knows that every watercourse has an individuality, which is no more to be analyzed than the personality of one's dearest friend. Two rivers may flow almost side by side for a hundred miles, separated only by a range of hills, and resemble each other no more than two women. You may admire the one, and grant it beauty and charm; but you will love the other, and dream of it, and desire infinite acquaintance of it.

These differences are too subtle for definition. Superficially, two rivers in the North Country are unlike only in this respect, that one has cut a deep valley through the hills and flows swiftly and shallowly to its sea, and the other has kept to the plateaus and drops leisurely by a series of cascades and short rapids, separated by long reaches of deep water. Otherwise their physical aspects coincide. The banks of archaic rock are covered with a thin soil which maintains so dense a tangle that the axe must clear a space for the smallest camp; their overhanging borders are of cedar and alder and puckerbush and osier; their waters are slightly colored by the juices of the swampland; following lines of minimum resistance, they twist gently or sharply every little way, and always to the voyager's delight, for the eye is unprepared for a beautiful vista, as the ear for a sudden and exquisite modulation in music.

So winds the Delectable River—

"through hollow lands and hilly lands"—

idly where the vale spreads out, quickly where the hills close in; black and mysterious in the deep places, frank and golden in the shoal. In one romantic open, where the stream flows thinly over a long stretch of sand, the bed is of an almost luminous amber, as if its particles had imprisoned a little of the sunlight that had fallen on them through the unnumbered years.

The River was somewhat low when I dipped paddle in it, and the ooze at the marge was a continuous chronicle of woodland life. Moose and deer, bear and beaver, mink and fisher, all the creatures of the wild had contributed to the narrative. Even the water had its tale: a line of bubbles would show that a large animal, likely a moose, had crossed a few minutes before our canoes rounded the bend. There were glimpses of less wary game: ducks and herons set sail at the last moment, and partridges, perching close at hand, cocked their foolish heads as we went by;

two otters sported on a bit of beach; trout leaped every rod of the way.

And never a sign of man or mark of man's destructiveness; nor axe nor fire had harmed a single tree. A journey of unmarred delight through a valley of unending green.

III.—SMUDGE.

"This," you say, as you step from the canoe and help to fling the cargo ashore, "this looks like good camping ground."

The place is more open than is usual, comparatively level, and a dozen feet above the river, which, brawling over a ledge, spreads into an attractive pool. The place also faces the west, where there is promise of a fine sunset; a number of large birches are in sight, and an abundance of balsam. "And," you remark, stooping to untie the tent-bag, "there are not many flies."

Instantly a mosquito sings in your ear, and as you still his song you recall a recent statement by the scientist Klein, that an insect's wings flap four hundred times in a second. The mind does not readily grasp so rapid a motion, but you accept the figures on trust, as you accept the distances of interstellar spaces.

Very soon you discover that you were in error about the fewness of the flies. They are all there—mosquitoes, black-flies, deer-flies, and

[71]

punkies, besides other species strictly vegetarian. So you drop the tent-bag and build a smudge. Experience has taught you to make a small but hot fire, and when this is well under way you kick open a rotted, moss-grown cedar and scoop up handfuls of damp mould. This, piled on and banked around the fire, provides a smudge that is continuous and effective. We built smudges morning, noon, and night. Whenever a halt was called, if only for five minutes, I reached mechanically for a strip of birchbark and a handful of twigs. At one camping place the ring of smudges suggested the magic fire circle in "Die Walküre." Brunhilde lay in her tent, in a reek of smoke, while Wotan, in no humor for song, heaped vegetable tinder upon the defending fires. More than once the darkening forest and the steel-gray sky of a Canadian twilight have set me humming the motives of "The Ring," and I shall always remember a pretty picture in an earlier cruise. "Jess" was a stable boy who drove our team to the point where roads ceased, and during a halt in the expedition this exuberant youth reclined upon a log, and with a pipe fashioned from a reed sought to imitate responsively the song of the white-throated sparrow. He looked for all the world like Siegfried in his forest.

"Smudge." It is not a poetic word—mere mention of it would distress Mr. Yeats; but it is potent as "Sesame" to unlock the treasures of memory. And before the laggard Spring comes round again many of us will sigh for a whiff of yellow, acrid smoke, curling from a smoldering fire in the heart of the enchanted wood.

IV.—"BOGWAH."

We have been paddling for more than an hour, through dark and slowly moving water. Two or three hundred yards has been the limit of the view ahead, as the stream swerves gracefully from the slightest rise of land, and flows now east, now north, now east, now south again. So long a stretch of navigable water is not common on the Delectable River, and we make the most of it, moving leisurely, and prisoning the everchanging picture with the imperfect camera of the eyes. Presently a too-familiar sound is heard above the dipping of the paddles, and the Indian at the stern announces, "Bogwah!"—which word in the tongue of the Chippewa signifies a shallow. And as we round the next bend we see the swifter water, the rocks in midstream, and the gently slanting line of treetops.

"Bogwah" spells work—dragging canoes over sandy and pebbly river-bottom, or unloading and carrying around the foam of perilous rapids. For compensation there is the pleasure of splashing ankle-deep and deeper in the cool current, and casting for trout in the "laughing shallow," which I much prefer to the "dreaming pool." They who choose it may fish from boat or ledge: for me, to wade and cast is the poetry of angling.

Assured that the "bogwah" before us extends for half a mile or more, we decide for luncheon, and the canoes are beached on an island, submerged in springtime, but at low water a heap of yellow sands. And I wish I might reconstruct for you the picture which memory too faintly outlines. Mere words will not do it, and yet one is impelled to try. "All literature," says Mr. Arnold Bennett, in one of his stimulating essays, "is the expression of feeling, of passion, of emotion, caused by a sensation of the interestingness of life. What drives a historian to write history? Nothing but the overwhelming impression forced upon him by the survey of past times. He is forced into an attempt to reconstitute the picture for others."

And so you are to imagine a marshy, brushy open, circular in shape, from which the hills and forest recede for a considerable distance, and into which a lazy brook comes to merge with the Delectable River; a place to which the moose travel in great numbers, as hoofmarks and cropped vegetation bear witness; a wild place, that must be wonderful in mist and moonlight. Now it is drenched with sunrays from a vaporless sky, and the white-throat is singing all around us—not the usual three sets of three notes, but seven triplets. Elsewhere on the River, days apart, I heard that prolonged melody, and although I have looked in the bird books for record of so sustained a song, I have not found it.

V.—FINE FEATHERS.

There is a certain school of anglers that go about the business of fishing with much gravity. You should hear the Great Neal discourse of their profundities. Lacking that privilege, you may conceive a pair of these anglers met beside a river, seeking to discover which of the many insects flying about is preferred by the trout on that particular morning. There is disagreement, or there is lack of evidence. It is decided to catch a trout, eviscerate him, and obtain internal and indisputable evidence. For the cast any fly is used, and when the trout is opened it is learned that he has been feeding on a small black insect; whereupon our anglers tie a number of flies to resemble that insect, and proceed solemnly with their day's work. Though the trout scorn their fine feathers, they will not fish with any fly.

With the subtleties of this school I have no sympathy. They might be of profit on waters that are much fished, but they are wasted on the

[75]

wilderness, where the trout will rise to almost any lure. When I make an expedition I take along two or three dozen flies, for the mere pleasure of looking at them, and rearranging them in the fly-book; but I wet less than half a dozen. On the Delectable River we cast only when trout are needed for the frypan. You are to picture canoes drawn up on a sandbar, and a ribbon of black smoke curling from a strip of birch bark that marks the beginning of a fire. It is time to get the fish. So I set up my rod and walk up-stream perhaps a hundred yards, casting on the current where it cuts under the farther bank. Al-most every cast evokes a trout; this one takes the tail fly, a Silver Doctor, the next one strikes the Bucktail dropper; any other flies would serve. The largest fish is taken on my return, from under the stern of one of the canoes. Where trout are so plentiful and so unwary, there is no call for the preparatory work of the evisceration school of anglers.

My reason for using a dropper fly is not to offer the trout two counterfeit insects differing in shape or color; as commonly attached to the leader, the dropper swims with the tail fly. "Sir," said the Great Neal, in the manner of Samuel Johnson, "when the dropper is properly attached, as I attach it, two aspects of the lure are presented to the fish, the one fly moving through the water, the other dancing an inch or so above.   This, Sir, is how I tie it."

And sitting at the Oracle's feet, ye learn "all ye need to know."

VI.—THALASSA!

Trails there are that one remembers from their beginnings to their ends, because of the variety and charm of the pictures offered along the way.   Monotony marks the trails that fade from memory; they represent hours of marching through timber of a second growth, or skirting hills where dead sticks stand forlorn and only the fireweed blooms.   Of rememberable roads the last stage of our journey to the Great Water is the one I have now in mind.   It is the longest carry, two miles or less, sharply down hill, though less precipitate than the river, which, after many days of idling, now flings itself impatiently toward the shore.   We linger where it makes its first great leap.   Many have come thus far from the south, and, looking on the shallow pool beyond, have decided that there is no profit in going farther; or they have explored a bit and, encountering *bogwah,* have reached the same conclusion. Who would conjecture that past the shallows lie leagues of deep and winding waters, reserved by nature as a reward for the adventurer who counts a glimpse of the unknown worth all the labor of

[77]

the day? We who have come from the head waters know that nature has as wisely screened the river's source. Where the lake ends is a forbidding tangle of water shrubs and timber; the outlet is an archipelago of sharp rocks, and the stream, if found, is seen to be small and turbulent.

The last carry keeps the Delectable River in view; foam, seen through the firs, marks its plunging flight. And then we draw away from it for a space, and cross an open thickly strewn with great stones, a sunlit place, where berries and a few flowers are privileged to exist. A little time is spent here in picking up the trail, which has spilled itself among the stones; then, the narrow footway regained, we drop as quickly as the river, and presently our feet touch sand. We break through a fringe of evergreens and cry out as the Greeks cried out when they saw the sea. The lake at last!—

> *The river, done with wandering,*
> *The silver, silent shore.*

A LINE-O'-TYPE OR TWO

"Lord, what fools these mortals be."

ARMS AND THE COLYUM.

I SING of arms and heroes, not because
    I'm thrilled by what these heroes do or die for:
The Colyum's readers think they make its laws,
And I make out to give them what they cry for.

And since they cry for stuff about the war,
Since war at this safe distance not to *them*'s hell,
I have to write of things that I abhor,
And far, strange battlegrounds like Ypres and Przemysl.

War is an almost perfect rime for bore;
And, 'spite my readers (who have cursed and blessed me),
Some day I'll throw the war junk on the floor,
And write of things that really interest me:

Of books in running brooks, and wilding wings,
Of music, stardust, children, casements giving
On seas unvext by wars, and other things
That help to make our brief life worth the living.

I sing of arms and heroes, just because
All else is shadowed by that topic fearful;
But I've a mind to chuck it [Loud applause],
And tune my dollar harp to themes more cheerful.

[79]

LISTEN, Laura, Mary, Jessica, Dorothy, and other sweet singers! Gadder Roy, who is toiling over the pitcher-and-bowl circuit, wishes that some poet would do a lyric on that salvation of the traveler, Ham and Eggs. He doubts that it can be done by anybody who has not, time out of mind, scanned a greasy menu in a greasier hashery, and finally made it h. and e.

WE FEARED WE HAD STARTED SOMETHING.

Sir: Should G. E. Thorpe's typewritten communications carrying the suggestion GET/FAT precede or follow our communications which carry EAT/ME? E. A. T.

THEY'RE OFF!

Sir: What position in your letter file, respecting the suggestions of GET/FAT, will my typewritten letters land, as they end thusly: "HEL/NO"? H. E. L.

SWEETLY INEFFECTIVE.

Sir: Perhaps the reason my collection letters have so little effect lately is that these cheerless communications always conclude with JAM/JAR.
J. A. M.

BUT APROPOS.

Sir: All this GET/FAT excitement reminds me of the case, so old it's probably new again, of

[80]

one Simmons, who wrote letters for one Green, and signed them "Green, per Simmons."

W. S.

SORRY. THERE WERE SEVERAL IN LINE AHEAD OF YOU.

Sir: I have been waiting, very patiently, for some one to inform you that the sincerity of A. L. Lewis, manager of the country elevator department of the Quaker Oats Company, is sometimes made questionable by the initials, ALL/ GAS, appearing on his business correspondence.

O. K.

THE SECOND POST.
[Received by a clothing company.]

Dear Sirs: I received the suits you sent me but in blue not gray as I said. Don't try to send me your refuss, I am sending them back. I ain't color blind or a jack ass, you shouldn't treat me as that. I understand your wife is making coats for ladies now. Have her make one (dark) for my wife who is a stout 42 with a fer neck. Now send me what I asked for, the old woman is perticular. The trousers you sent wouldn't slip over my head. Ever faithful, etc.

For Academy Ghost, or Familiar Spirit, P. D. Q. nominates Miss Bessie Spectre of Boston.

"THE lake is partially frozen over and well filled with skaters."—Janesville Gazette.

> Three children sliding on the ice,
>   Upon a summer's day,
> As it fell out, they all fell in,
>   The rest they ran away.
>
> MA GOOSE.

THERE is plenty of snap to the department of mathematics in the Shortridge high school in Indianapolis. The head of the department is Walter G. Gingery.

WEDDED, in Chicago, Otho Neer and Lucille Dimond. Fashion your own setting.

OH, dear! Rollin Pease, the singer, is around again, reminding sundry readers of the difficulty of keeping them on a knife.

"THOSE FLAPJACKS OF BROWN'S."
(*Postscriptum.*)

> I'll write no more verses—plague take 'em!—
>   Court neither your smiles nor your frowns,
> If you'll only please tell how to make 'em,
>   Those flapjacks of Brown's.
>
> D. W. A.

> Three cupfuls of flour will do nicely,
>   And toss in a teaspoon of salt;
> Next add baking powder, precisely
>   Two teaspoons, the stuff to exalt;

Of sugar two tablespoons, heaping—
    (All spoons should be heaping, says Neal);
Then mix it with strokes that are sweeping,
    And stir like the Deil.

Three eggs. (Tho' the missus may sputter,
    You'll pay to her protest no heed.)
A size-of-an-egg piece of butter,
    And milk as you happen to need.
Now mix the whole mess with a beater;
    Don't get it too thick or too thin.
(And I pause to remark that this meter
    Is awkward as sin.)

Of course there are touches that only
    A genius like Brown can impart;
And genius is everywhere lonely,
    And no one but Brown has the art.
I picture him stirring—a gentle
    Exponent of modern Romance,
With his shirttails, in style Oriental,
    Outside of his pants.

THE DICTATERS.

Sir: I have lost a year's growth since I went into business in answering questions about the letters that appear after my communications—HAM/AND.   H. A. M.

LETTERS from the vice-president of the Badger Talking Machine Company of Milwaukee are signed JAS/AK. What do you make of that, Watsonius?

[83]

THE following was typed at the end of a letter received t'other day: "HEE/HA."

RECURRING to the dictaters, letters from the O'Meara Paper company of New York are tagged JEW/EM.

> IRENE, she works for David Meyer,
>   Likes her job, not peeved a bit.
> But when she ends a letter she
>   Marks it with this sign, DAM/IT.
>
> FERRO.

HINT to students in the School of Journalism: Always begin the description of a tumultuous scene by saying that it is indescribable, and then proceed to describe it until the telegraph editor chokes you off.

To our young friend who expects to operate a column: Lay off the item about Miss Hicks entertaining Carrie Dedbeete and Ima Proone; it is phony. But the wheeze about the "eternal revenue collector" is still good, and timely.

"I AM a cub reporter," writes W. H. D., "and am going to conduct a column in a few weeks, I think." Zazzo? Well, you can't do better than to start with the announcement that Puls & Puls are dentists in Sheboygan. And you might add that if the second Puls is a son the firm should be Puls & Fils.

[84]

Our cub reporter friend, W. H. D., who expects to run a column presently, should not overlook the sure-fire wheeze, "Shoes shined on the inside."

Still undiscouraged by the failure of his "shoes shined on the inside" wheeze to get by, the new contrib hopefully sends us the laundry slogan: "Don't kill your wife. Let us do the dirty work."

When all the world is safe for democracy, only the aristocracy of taste will remain, and this will cover the world. There is hardly a town so small that it does not contain at least one member. All races belong to it, and its passwords are accepted in every capital. Its mysteries are Rosicrucian to persons without taste. And no other aristocracy was ever, or ever will be, so closely and sympathetically knit together.

Whether Europe and Latin America like it or not, the Monroe Doctrine must and shall be preserved. You may remember the case of the man who was accused of being a traitor. It was charged that he had spoken as disrespectfully of the Monroe Doctrine as Jeffrey once spoke of the Equator. This the man denied vigorously. He avowed that he loved the Monroe Doctrine, that he was willing to fight for it, and, if neces-

sary, to die for it. All he had said was that he
didn't know what it was about.

"There will be no speeches. The entire
evening will be given over to entertainment."—
Duluth News-Tribune.

At least prohibition is a check on oratory.

We have just been talking to an optimist, whose
nerves have been getting shaky. We fancy that
a straw vote of the rocking-chair fleet on a sanitarium porch would show a preponderance of op-
timists. What brought them there? Worry,
which is brother to optimism. We attribute our
good health and reasonable amount of hair to the
fact that we never flirted with optimism, except
for a period of about five years, during which
time we lost more hair than in all the years since.

May we again point out that pessimism is the
only cheerful philosophy? The pessimist is not
concerned over the so-called yellow peril—at
least the pessimist who subscribes to the theory
of the degradation of energy. Europe is losing
its pep, but so is Asia. There may be a difference of degree, but not enough to keep one from
sleeping soundly o' nights. The twentieth or
twenty-first century can not produce so energetic
a gang as that which came out of Asia in the fifth
century.

"If I had no duties," said Dr. Johnson, "and no reference to futurity, I would spend my life in driving briskly in a postchaise with a pretty woman." And we wonder whether the old boy, were he living now, would choose, instead, a Ford.

In time of freeze prepare for thaw. And no better advice can be given than Doc Robertson's: "Keep your feet dry and your gutters open."

There was an Irish meeting in Janesville the other night, and the press reported that "Garlic songs were sung." And we recall another report of a lecture on Yeats and the Garlic Revival. Just a moment, while we take a look at the linotype keyboard. . . .

THINGS WORTH KNOWING.

Sir: A method of helping oneself to soda crackers, successfully employed by a traveling man, may be of interest to your boarding house readers. Slice off a small piece of butter, leaving it on the knife, then reach across the table and slap the cracker.   V.

By the way, Bismarck had a solution of the Irish problem which may have been forgotten. He proposed that the Irish and the Dutch exchange countries. The Dutch, he said, would make a garden of Ireland. "And the Irish?" he was asked. "Oh," he replied, "the Irish would neglect the dikes."

A CITY is known by the newspapers it keeps. They reflect the tastes of the community, and if they are lacking in this or that it is because the community is lacking. And so it is voxpoppycock to complain that a newspaper is not what a small minority thinks it ought to be. The fault, dear Brutus, is not in our journals, but in ourselves, that we are underlings.

Dissatisfaction with American newspapers began with the first one printed, and has been increasing steadily since. In another hundred years this dissatisfaction may develop into positive annoyance.

WE tried to have a sign in Los Onglaze translated into French for the benefit of Lizy, the linotype operator who sets this column in Paris, and who says she has yet to get a laugh out of it, but two Frenchmen who tried their hand at it gave it up. Perhaps the compositor at the adjacent machine can randmacnally it for Lizy. Here is the enseigne:

"Flannels washed without shrinking in the rear."

To the fair Murine: "Drink to me only with thine eyes."

"HOSIERY for Easter," declares an enraptured ad writer in the Houston Post, "reaches new heights of loveliness."

IF the persons who parade around with placards announcing that this or that shop is "unfair" were to change the legend to read, "God is unfair," they might get a sympathetic rise out of us. We might question the assertion that in creating men unequal the Creator was actuated by malice rather than a sense of humor, but we should not insist on the point.

THE SECOND POST.
[Received by a construction company.]

Dear Sir I an writhing you and wanted to know that can I get a book from your company which will teach me of oprating steam and steam ingean. I was fireing at a plant not long ago and found one of your catalogs and it give me meny good idol about steam. I have been opiratin stean for the last 12 years for I know that there are lots more to learn about steam and I want to learn it so I will close for this time expecting to here from you soon.

"SINCE Frank Harris has been mentioned," communicates C. E. L., "it would be interesting to a lot of folks to know just what standing he has in literature." Oh, not much. Aside from being one of the best editors the Saturday Review ever had, one of the best writers of short stories in English or any other language, and one of the most acute critics in the profession, his standing is negligible.

OUR young friend who is about to become a colyumist should certainly include in his first string the restaurant wheeze: "Don't laugh at our coffee. You may be old and weak yourself some day."

"ONE sinister eye—the right one—gleamed at him over the pistol."—Baltimore Sun.

No wonder foreigners have a hard time with the American language.

BALLADE OF THE OUBLIETTE.

And deeper still the deep-down oubliette,
Down thirty feet below the smiling day.
                              —*Tennyson.*

                    Sudden in the sun
An oubliette winks. Where is he? Gone.
                              —*Mrs. Browning.*

Gaoler of the donjon deep—
Black from pit to parapet—
In whose depths forever sleep
Famous bores whose sun has set,

Daily ope the portal; let
In the bores who daily bore.
Thrust—sans sorrow or regret—
Thrust them through the Little Door.

Warder of Oblivion's keep—
Dismal dank, and black as jet—
Through the fatal wicket sweep
All the pests we all have met.
Prithee, overlook no bet;
Grab them—singly, by the score—
And, lest they be with us yet,
Thrust them through the Little Door.

Lead them to the awful leap
With a merry chansonette;
Push them blithely off the steep;
We'll forgive them and forget.
Toss them, like a cigarette,
To the far Plutonian floor.
Drop them where they'll cease to fret—
Thrust them through the Little Door.

Keeper of the Oubliette,
Wouldst thou have us more and more
In thine everlasting debt—
Thrust them through the Little Door.

To insure the safety of the traveling public, the
Maroon Taxicab Company is putting out a line of
armored cabs. These will also be equipped with
automatic brakes, so that when a driver for a

rival taxicab company shoots a Maroon, the cab will come to a stop.

A NEAT and serviceable Christmas gift is a sawed-off shotgun. Carried in your limousine, it may aid in saving your jewels when returning from the opera.

"THE entertainment committee of the Union League Club," so it says, "is with considerable effort spending some of your money to please you." In the clubs to which we belong there is no observable effort.

CERTAIN toadstools are colored a pizenous pink underneath; a shade which is also found on the cheeks of damosels and dames whom you see on the avenue. Poor kalsomining, we call it.

WHEN we begin to read a book, we begin with the title page; but many people, probably most, begin at "Chapter I." We have recommended books to friends, and they have read them; and then they have said, "Tell me something about the author." The preface would have told them, but they do not read prefaces. Do you?

ALTHOUGH ongweed to the extinction point by the subject of names, we have no right to assume that the subject is not of lively interest to other people. So let it be recorded that George Demon was arrested in Council Bluffs for beating his wife. Also, Miss Elsie Hugger is director of dancing in the Ithaca Conservatory of Music. Furthermore, S. W. Henn of the Iowa State College was selected as a judge for the National Poultry Show. Moreover, G. O. Wildhack is in the automobile business in Indianapolis, and Mrs. Cataract takes in washing in Peoria. Sleepy weather, isn't it?

SUCH A ONE MIGHT HAVE DRAWN PRIAM'S CURTAIN IN THE DEAD OF NIGHT, AND TOLD HIM HALF HIS TROY WAS BURNED.

[From the Eagle Grove, Ia., Eagle.]

The Rev. Winter was pastor of the M. E. Church many years ago, at the time it was destroyed by a cyclone. Engineer Sam Wood broke the news to Mr. Winter gently by shouting: "Your church has all blown to hell, Elder!"

THE ENRAPTURED REPORTER.

[From the Lewisville, Ark., Recorder.]

The evening was most propitious. The air was balmy. The fragrance of flowers was patent in the breeze. The limpid moonlight, in a glow of beauty, kissed the hills and valleys. While from the vines and bushes the merry twitter of playful birds, symphonies soft and low, entranced with other delight, the romantic party goers. Now a

[93]

still other delight was in store—some fine music and good singing, which every recipient enjoyed to the highest note. Thanks and compliments for such a model evening were ornate and lavish and all left truly glad that they had been.

FULL OF HIS SUBJECT.

[From the Evansville, Ind., Courier.]

Dr. Hamilton A. Hymes, pastor of Grace Memorial Presbyterian church, has recovered from a recent illness, caused from a carbuncle on his neck. His subject for Sunday night will be "Is There a Hell?"

THAT TRIOLET DRIVEL.

Will you can it or no?—
    That Triolet drivel.
It irritates so.
Will you can it or no?
For the habit may grow,
    And the thought makes me snivel.
Will you can it or no?—
    That Triolet drivel.

D. A. D. BURNITT.

Yes, we'll can it or no,
    As the notion may seize us.
If a thing is de trop,
Yes; we'll can it—or no.

> For we always let go
>> When a thing doesn't please us.
> Yes, we'll can it, or—no,
>> As the notion may seize us.

SIR OLIVER LODGE has seen so many tables move and heard so many tambourines, that he now keeps an open mind on miracles. We hope he believes that the three angels appeared to Joan of Arc, as that is our favorite miracle. Had they appeared only once we might have doubted the apparition; but, as we remember the story, they appeared three times.

SIR OLIVER may be interested in a case reported to us by L. J. S. His company had issued a tourist policy to a lady who lost her trunk on the way to Tulsa, Okla., and who put in a claim for $800. The adjuster at Dallas wrote:

"Assured is the famous mind reader, and one of her best stunts is answering questions in regard to the location of stolen property, but she was unable to be of any assistance to me."

SOME of the members of the Cosmopolitan club are about as cosmopolitan as the inhabitants of Cosmopolis, Mich.

AT the request of a benedick we are rushing to the Cannery by parcel-post Jar 617: "Don't they make a nice-looking couple!"

ENGLISH AS SHE IS MURDERED.

Sir: After Pedagogicus' class gets through with Senator Borah's masterpiece, it might look over this legend which the Herald and Examiner has been carrying: "Buy bonds like the victors fought." E. E. E.

THE Illinois War Savings Bulletin speaks of "personal self-interest." This means you!

"GRADUATION from the worst to the best stuff," is Mr. W. L. George's method of acquiring literary taste. Something can be said for the method, and Mr. George says it well, and we are sorry, in a manner of speaking, not to believe a word of it; unless, as is possible, we both believe the same thing fundamentally. Taste, in literature and music, and in other things, is, we are quite sure, natural. It can be trained, but this training is a matter of new discoveries. A taste that has to be led by steps from Owen Meredith to George Meredith, which could not recognize the worth of the latter before passing through the former, is no true taste. Graduation from the simple to the complex is compatible with a natural taste, but this simple may be first class, as much music and literature is. New forms of beauty may puzzle the possessor of natural taste, but not for long. He does not require preparation in inferior stuff.

Speaking of George Meredith, we are told again (they dig the thing up every two or three years) that, when a reader for Chapman & Hall, he turned down "East Lynne," "Erewhon," and other books that afterward became celebrated. What of it? Meredith may not have known anything about literature, but he knew what he liked. Moreover, he was a marked and original writer, and as that tolerant soul, Jules Lemaitre, has noted, the most marked and original of writers are those who do not understand everything, nor feel everything, nor love everything, but those whose knowledge, intelligence, and tastes have definite limitations.

BUT WOULD IT NOT REQUIRE A GEOLOGIC PERIOD?

Sir: You are kind enough to refer to my lecture on "Literary Taste and How to Acquire It." I venture to suggest that your summary—viz.: "It is to read only first-class stuff," not only fails to meet the problem, but represents exactly the view that I am out to demolish. If, as I presume, you mean that the ambitious person who now reads Harold Bell Wright should sit down to the works of Shakespeare, I can tell you at once that the process will be a failure. My method is one of graduation from the worst to the best stuff.

W. L. George.

[97]

WE do not wish to crab W. L. George's act, "Literary Taste and How to Acquire It," but we know the answer. It is to read only first-class stuff. Circumstances may oblige a man to write second-class books, but there is no reason why he should read such.

THE STORM.

(By a girl of ten years.)

It lightnings, it thunders
And I go under,
And where do I go,
I wonder.

I go, I go—
I know.
Under the covers,
That's where I go.

The little poet of the foregoing knew where she was going, which is more than can be said for many modern bards.

THE EIGHTH VEIL.

(By J-mes Hun-k-r.)

There was a wedding under way. From the bright-lit mansion came the evocations of a loud bassoon. Ulick Guffle, in whom the thought of matrimony always produced a bitter nausea, glowered upon the house and spat acridly upon the

pave. "Imbeciles! Humbugs! Romantic rot!"
he raged.

Three young men drew toward the scene.
Ulick barred their way, but two of the trio slipped
by him and escaped. The third was nailed by
Guffle's glittering eye. Ulick laid an ineluctable
hand upon the stranger's arm. "Listen!" he commanded. "Matrimony and Art are sworn and
natural foes. Ingeborg Bunck was right; there
are no illegitimate children; all children are valid.
Sounds like Lope de Vega, doesn't it? But it
isn't. It is Bunck. Whitman, too, divined the
truth. Love is a germ; sunlight kills it. It needs
l'obscurité and a high temperature. As Baude-
laire said—or was it Maurice Barrès?—dans la
nuit tous les chats sont gris. Remy de Gour-
mont . . ."

The wedding guest beat his shirtfront; he could
hear the bassoon doubling the cello. But Ulick
continued ineluctably. "Woman is a sink of
iniquity. Only Gounod is more loathsome. That
Ave Maria—Grand Dieu! But Frédéric Chopin,
nuance, cadence, appoggiatura—there you have
it. En amour, les vieux fous sont plus fous que
les jeunes. Listen to Rochefoucauld! And Mon-
taigne has said, C'est le jouir et non le posséder
qui rend heureux. And Pascal has added, Les
affaires sont les affaires. As for Stendhal, Flaubert, Nietzsche, Edgar Saltus, Balzac, Gautier,

[99]

Dostoievsky, Rabelais, Maupassant, Anatole France, Bourget, Turgenev, Verlaine, Renan, Walter Pater, Landor, Cardinal Newman and the Brothers Goncourt . . ."

Ulick seized his head with both hands, and the wedding guest seized the opportunity to beat it, as the saying is. "Swine!" Ulick flung after him. "Swine, before whom I have cast a hatful of pearls!" He spat even more acridly upon the pave and turned away. "After all," he growled, "Stendhal was right. Or was it Huysmans? No, it was neither. It was Cambronne."

THOUGH there has been little enough to encourage it, the world is growing kinder; at least friendliness is increasing. Every other day we read of some woman living pleasantly in a well appointed apartment, supplied with fine raiment and an automobile, the fruit of Platonism. "No," she testifies, "there was nothing between us. He was merely a friend."

WHAT heaven hath cleansed let no man put asunder. Emma Durdy and Raymond Bathe, of Nokomis, have been j. in the h. b. of w.

THE TRACERS ARE AT WORK.

Sir: Please consult the genealogical files of the Academy and advise me if Mr. Harm Poppen of

Gurley, Nebraska, is a lineal descendant of the
w. k. Helsa Poppen, famous in profane history.

E. E. M.

OUR opinion, already recorded, is that if Keats
had spent fifteen or twenty minutes more on his
Grecian Urn, all of the stanzas would be as good
as three of them. And so we think that if A. B.
had put in, say, a half hour more on her sonnet
she would not have rhymed "worldliness" and
"moodiness." Of the harmony, counterpoint, thor-
oughbass, etc., of verse we know next to nothing
—we play on *our* tin whistle entirely by ear—but
there are things which we avoid, perhaps need-
lessly. One of these is the rhyming of words like
utterly, monody, lethargy, etc.; these endings
seem weak when they are bunched. Our assist-
ants will apprehend that we are merely offering
a suggestion or two, which we hope they will follow up by exploring the authorities.

MUSIC like Brahms' Second Symphony is pecul-
iarly satisfying to the listener. The first few
measures disclose that the composer is in complete
control of his ideas and his expression of them.
He has something to say, and he says it without
uncertainty or redundancy. Only a man who *has*
something to say may dare to say it only once.

THOSE happy beings who "don't know a thing about art, but know what they like," are restricted to the obvious because of ignorance of form; their enjoyment ends where that of the cultivated person begins. Take music. The person who knows what he likes takes his pleasure in the tune, but gets little or nothing from the tune's development; hence his favorite music is music which is all tune.

We recall a naïve query by the publisher of a magazine, at a musicale in Gotham. Our hostess, an accomplished pianist, had played a Chopin Fantasia, and the magazine man was expressing his qualified enjoyment. "What I can't understand," said he, "is why the tune quits just when it's running along nicely." This phenomenon, no doubt, has mystified thousands of other "music lovers."

A BOSTON woman complains that school seats have worn out three pairs of pants (her son's) in three months. "Is a wheeze about the seat of learning too obvious?" queries Genevieve. Oh, quite too, my dear!

MR. FREDERICK HARRISON at 89 observes: "May my end be early, speedy, and peaceful! I regret nothing done or said in my long and busy life. I withdraw nothing, and, as I said before, am not conscious of any change in mind. In youth I was called a revolutionary; in old age I am called a reactionary; both names alike untrue. . . . I ask nothing. I seek nothing. I fear nothing. I have done and said all that I ever could have done and said. There is nothing more. I am ready, and await the call."

A very good prose version of Henley's well known poem. As for regretting nothing, a man at forty would be glad to unsay and undo many things. At seventy, and decidedly at eighty-nine, these things have so diminished in importance that it is not worth while withdrawing them.

A DAY WITH LORD DID-MORE.

"Mr. Hearst is the home brew; no other hope."
—The Trib.

At his usual hour Lord Did-More rose—
Renewed completely by repose—
His pleasant duty to rehearse
Of oiling up the universe.

Casting a glance aloft, he saw
That, yielding to a natural law,
The sun obediently moved
Precisely as he had approved.

If mundane things would only run
As regularly as the Sun!
But Earth's affairs, less nicely planned,
Require Lord Did-More's guiding hand.

This day, outside Lord Did-More's door,
There waited patiently a score
Of diplomats from far and near
Who sought his sympathetic ear.

Each brought to him, that he might scan,
The latest governmental plan,
And begged of him a word or two
Approving what it hoped to do.

Lord Did-More nodded, smiled or frowned,
Some word of praise or censure found,
Withheld or added his "O. K."
And sent the ministers away.

These harmonized and sent away,
Lord Did-More finished up his day
By focusing his cosmic brain
On our political campaign.

And night and morning, thro' the land,
The public prints at his command
Proclaimed, in type that fairly burst,
The doughty deeds of Did-More Hearst.

THE SECOND POST.

[From a genius in Geneseo, Ill.]

Dear sir: I am the champion Cornhusker I
have given exhibitions in different places and theater managers and moveing picture men have asked
me why I dont have my show put into moves
(Film). I beleave it would make a very inter-

esting Picture. We could have it taken right in the Cornfield and also on the stage. It would be very interesting for farmer boys and would be a good drawing card in small towns. I beleave we could make 1000 feet of it by showing me driveing into the field with my extra made wagon. then show them my style and speed of husking and perheps let a common husker husk a while. I could also give my exibition on the stage in a theater includeing the playing of six or eight different Instruments. For instence when I plow with a traction engine or tresh I also lead bands and Orchestra's.

THERE is a stage in almost everybody's musical education when Chopin's Funeral March seems the most significant composition in the world.

THE two stenogs in the L coach were discussing the opera. "I see," said one, "that they're going to sing 'Flagstaff.'" "That's Verdi's latest opera," said the other. "Yes," contributed the gentleman in the adjacent seat, leaning forward; "and the scene is laid in Arizona."

MR. SHANKS voxpops that traffic should be relieved, not prevented, as "the automobile is absolutely important in modern business life." Now, the fact is that the automobile has become a nuisance; one can get about much faster and cheaper in the city on Mr. Shanks' w. k. mare. Life to-day is scaled to the automobile, whereas, as our gossip Andy Rebori contends, it ought to be scaled to the baby carriage. Many lines of industry are short of labor because this labor has been withdrawn for the care of automobiles.

"Do you remember," asks a fair correspondent (who protests that she is only academically fair), "when we used to read 'A Shropshire Lad,' and A. E., and Arthur Symons, and Yeats? And you used to print so many of the beautiful things they wrote?" Ah, yes, we do remember; but that, my dear, was a long, long time ago, in the period which has just closed, as Bennett puts it. How worth while those things used to seem, and what pleasant days those were. Men say that they will come again. But men said that Arthur would come again.

OUR method: We select only things that interest us, assuming that other people will be interested; if they are not—why, chacun à son goût, as the cannibal king remarked, adding a little salt. We printed "The Spires of Oxford" a long time ago because it interested us exceedingly.

A VALUED colleague quotes the emotional line—
  "This is my own, my native land!"—

as palliation, if not justification, for the "simple, homely, and comprehensive adjuration, 'Own Your Own Home.'" We acknowledge the homeliness and comprehensiveness, but we deny the value of poetic testimony. Said Dr. Johnson:

> "Let observation with extensive view
> Survey mankind from China to Peru,"

which, De Quincey or Tennyson declared, should have run: "Let observation with extended observation observe mankind extensively." Poets and tautology go walking like the Walrus and the Carpenter.

BOLSHEVISM OF LONG AGO.

"A radical heaven is a place where every man does what he pleases, and there is a general division of property every Saturday night."— George S. Hillard (1853).

LULLABY.

In Woodman, Wis., the Hotel Lull
Is where a man may rest his skull.
All care and fret is void and null
When one puts up at Hotel Lull.
Ah, might I wing it as a gull
Unto the mansion kept by Lull—
By W. K. Lull, the w. k. Lull,
Who greets the guests at Hotel Lull.

[107]

"A THING of beauty is a joy forever." But if, miraculously, it happens in Chicago, it can, despite the poet's word, "pass into nothingness." The old Field Museum, seen beneath a summer moon, when the mist is on the lake, is as beautiful as anything on the earth's crust. Not to preserve the exterior were a sin against Beauty, which is the unforgivable sin.

"LEMME UP, DARLING! LEMME UP!"
[From the Detroit Free Press.]

My advertisement of Feb. 24 was error. I will be responsible for my wife's debts.

Leo Tyo.

"I'LL make the Line some day or jump into Great Salt Lake," warns C. W. O. Pick out a soft spot, friend. We jumped into it one day and sprained an ankle.

Alice in Cartoonland.

I.

"HELLO!" said the Hatter. "I haven't seen you for a long time."

"No," said Alice; "I've been all over—in Wonderland, in Bookland, in Stageland, and forty other lands. People must be tired of my adventures. Where am I now? I never know."

"In Cartoonland," said the Hatter.

"And what are *you* doing here?" inquired Alice.

"I'm searching for an original cartoon idea," replied the Hatter. "Would you like to come along?"

"Ever so much," said Alice.

"The first thing we have to do is to get across that chasm," said the Hatter, pointing.

Alice saw a huge legend on the far wall of the chasm, and spelled it out—"O-b-l-i-v-i-o-n."

"Yes, Oblivion," said the Hatter. "That's where they dump defeated candidates and other undesirables. Come on, we can cross a little below here."

He indicated a thin plank that lay across the Chasm of Oblivion.

"Will it hold us?" said Alice.

"It has held the G. O. P. Elephant and the Democratic Donkey, and all sorts of people and things. Let's hurry over, as here comes the Elephant now, with Mr. Taft riding it, and the plank *might* give way."

II.

"By the way," said the Hatter, "here is my hat store."

There were only two kinds in the window— square paper caps and high silk hats. Alice had never seen paper caps before.

"They're worn by the laboring man," said the Hatter; "but you never see them outside of Cartoonland. The plug hats are for Capitalists. I also keep whiskers; siders for Capital and ordinary for Labor."

"O, there's a railroad train!" said Alice, suddenly.

"No use taking that train," said the Hatter; "it doesn't go. Did you ever see an engine like that outside Cartoonland? And even if it did work we shouldn't get very far, as the rock Obstruction is always on the track."

"I'd just as soon walk," said Alice.

III.

"Mercy! there's a giant!" exclaimed Alice.

"Don't be alarmed," said the Hatter; "he's perfectly good natured."

"What an awful-looking creature!" said Alice.

"He's awfully out of drawing," said the Hatter, critically; "but, then, almost everything in Cartoonland is. It's the idea that counts."

"You said you were searching for an original idea," Alice reminded him.

"But I don't expect to find one," the Hatter replied. "You see, it wouldn't be any use; nobody would understand it. People like the old familiar things, you know."

"Still, we might happen on one," said Alice. "Let's walk along."

IV.

Suddenly a door opened, and a great quantity of rubbish was swept briskly into the street.

"That's the New Broom," said the Hatter. "There's been another election. Evidently the Democrats won, as there goes the Donkey, waving his ears and hee-hawing."

"Oh, is that a fruit store?" asked Alice.

"No; the Republican headquarters," replied the Hatter. "That huge cornucopia you see is a symbol of Prosperity. Prosperity in Cartoonland is always represented by a horn of plenty with a pineapple in the muzzle. You've heard the expression, 'The pineapple of prosperity.' "

"No," said Alice, "but I've heard about the 'pineapple of politeness.' "

"That," said the Hatter, "is something else again."

V.

Presently they came to a collection of factories, the tall chimneys of which poured out smoke in great volume.

"Those are the Smoking Stacks of Industry," said the Hatter.

"What do they manufacture here?" asked Alice.

"Cartoonatums," said the Hatter. "A cartoonatum," he explained, "is a combination of wheels, rods, cogs, hoppers, cranks, etc., which sometimes looks like a sausage grinder and sometimes like a try-your-weight machine. It couldn't possibly go, any more than the locomotives in Cartoonland.

"Why don't the Cartoonlanders have machines that *can* go?" inquired Alice.

"That," replied the Hatter, "would require a little study and observation."

VI.

As Alice and the Hatter walked along they passed many curious things, such as Wolves in Sheep's Clothing, the skin of a Tiger nailed to a barn door, St. George and the Dragon, Father Knickerbocker, barrels of political mud, a huge serpent labeled "Anarchy," a drug store window full of bottles of Political Dope and boxes of Political Pills, an orchard of Political Plum Trees, and other objects which the Hatter said were as old as the hills. "I'm afraid there's nothing to hold us here," he declared.

Alice's attention was suddenly attracted by a little girl in a thin and ragged dress who, with an empty basket on her arm, was gazing wistfully at the goodies in a bakeshop window.

"She represents Poverty," said the Hatter. "When she isn't staring at a bakeshop she's looking at a proclamation by the ice trust, or something like that."

Alice spoke to the child and learned that she was one of a large family. Her father, she said, was a New York cartoonist who one day had been visited by an Original Idea.

"Where is he?" cried the Hatter excitedly.

"He dropped dead!" replied the child, weeping bitterly.

"Good night!" said the Hatter, and walked away.

A LINE-O'-TYPE OR TWO

Quicquid agunt homines nostri est farrago libelli.
—Juvenal.

QUESTION:

WHO is this Juvenal wheezer?
    Readers inquire every day.
Give us a line on the geezer—
    What is he trying to say?
Do you expect us to get stuff
    That is clear over our bean?
What is that *"Quicquid*, et cet." stuff?
    What does the gibberish mean?

REPLY:

If you're too lazy to look for
    Juvenal's name in the Dic,
Why should *I* go to the book for
    Such a cantankerous kick?
Still, to avoid all dissension,
    And my good nature to prove,
I am quite willing to mention
    One or two things about Juve.

Juve was a Roman humdinger,
    Writer of satires and sich.
He was consid'rable stinger—
    Rare were his sallies and rich.

[115]

High his poetic position,
  Lofty his manner and brow;
Lived in the time of Domitian;—
  That's all I think of just now.

As for that *"Quicquid,* and so forth,"
  I have but space to advise
If you'd decipher it go forth,
  Look in the Dic and be wise.
Make it a point, in your reading,
  Always to look up what's new.
That is a simple proceeding:
  Why not adopt it? *I* do.

IT HAS BEEN DONE.

Sir: Broke friend wife's favorite Victrola record. Told her about it. She came back with, "Well, that's the only record you ever broke." Do you think she was bawling me out or was she paying me a compliment?   E. P. P.

"WILL the Devil complete the capture of the modern church?" inquires the Rev. Mr. Straton of New York. Why is it assumed that the Old Boy is attempting to capture it? People go to the Devil; the Devil doesn't have to chase after them. The notion that Old Nick is always around drumming up business is an example of the inordinate vanity of man.

DEAN JONES of Yale is credited with this definition of freedom of speech: "The liberty to say what you think without thinking what you say."

"ON SUCH A NIGHT . . ."
[From the Bethany, Mo., Clipper.]

After the serving of light refreshments the young ladies repaired to the third floor and "tripped the light fantastic" while music waved eternal wands. And then the whole company flocked in and enjoyed the beauties of this grand home, lingering and chatting, with the enchanted spell of the glorious evening still strong upon each one, until the crescent moon had veiled her face and the vain young night trembled over her own beauty. And then with expressed regrets that the hours had flown so rapidly the guests bade a fair good night to their charming hostess.

TEMPERATURE.

An idea pushed along to us by L. O. K. has no doubt been seriously considered by the Congress. It is to move the tubes of all thermometers up an inch on the scale every fall, and down an inch in the spring. This would make our winter temperature much more endurable, and our summer temp. delightful.

LET US PERISH, RATHER, BY DEGREES.

Sir: Before the Congress adopts the idea of L. O. K. to move the tubes of all thermometers up an inch on the scale every fall and down an inch in the spring, I rush to inquire how shall we, who possess only a two inch thermometer, on which an inch covers at least 70 degrees, be able to withstand the extremes of climate? May I not suggest that the Congress be petitioned to make the move by degrees instead of inches, and thus avoid great suffering?   L. J. R.

You may have noted—nearly everybody else did—that Jean Paige and Albert Smith were married in Paris, Ill., "at the farm residence of Mr. and Mrs. Wigfall O'Hair." The Academy of Immortals attended in a body.

Commuters discuss many interesting topics, including the collection of garbage. Mac was reminded of a Michigan lady of his acquaintance who, with a new maid, was trying to pull off a very correct luncheon. In the midst of it the maid appeared and said, "Oh, Mrs. Kennedy, the garbage man wants a dime." The hostess, without batting an eye, replied: "We are having company to-day. Better get a quarter's worth."

" 'My mind is open on the question of garbage disposal,' Alderman Link declared."
You know what he means.

HYMN OF HATE.

(Reprinted at request of Mr. Hoover.)

Cranberry pie, or apricot—
We love them not, we hate them not.
Of all the victuals in pot or plate,
There's only one that we loathe and hate.
We love a hundred, we hate but one,
And that we'll hate till our race is run—
> BREAD PUDDING!

It's known to you all, it's known to you all,
It casts a gloom, and it casts a pall;
By whatso name they mark the mess,
You take one taste and you give one guess.
Come, let us stand in the Wailing Place,
A vow to register, face to face:
We will never forego our hate
Of that tasteless fodder we execrate—
> BREAD PUDDING!

Cranberry pie, or apricot—
Some folks like 'em, and some folks not.
They're not so bad if they're made just right,
Tho' they don't enkindle our appetite.
But *you* we hate with a lasting hate,
And never will we that hate abate:
Hate of the tooth and hate of the gum,
Hate of palate and hate of tum,
Hate of the millions who've choked you down,
In country kitchen or house in town.
We love a thousand, we hate but one,
With a hate more hot than the hate of Hun—
> BREAD PUDDING!

SINCE prohibition came in, says the Onion King, Americans have taken to eating onions. As Lincoln prophesied, this nation is having a new breath of freedom.

ASKED what the racket was all about, the inspired waiter at the Woman's Athletic Club replied, "It's the Vassar illumini."

IN a soi-disant democracy "personal liberty" is an empty phrase, bursting with nothingness. Personal liberty is to be enjoyed only under a benevolent autocracy. It is contained wholly in the code of King Pausole:

"I.—Ne nuis pas à ton voisin.

"II.—Ceci bien compris, fais ce qu'il te plaît."

THERE are many definitions of "optimist" and "pessimist." As good as another is one that the Hetman of the Boul Mich Cossacks is fond of quoting: "An optimist is a man who sees a great light where there is none. A pessimist is a man who comes along and blows out the light."

"TWO-PIANO playing is more or less of a sport, as the gardeners say," observes Mr. Aldrich in the New York Times. And we are reminded of Philip Hale's review of a two-piano recital. "We have heard these two gentlemen separately without being greatly stirred," he said in effect, "but their combination was like bringing together the component parts of a seidlitz powder."

WRITES H. D., at present in Loz Onglaze: "Alphonse Daudet says that the sun is the real liar, that it alone is responsible for all the exaggerations of its favorite children of the south." And you know what the sun does to Californians.

THE Paris decision suggests a neat form letter for collection lawyers: "We hope that you will not place us under the necessity of envisaging the grave situation which will be created if you persist in failing to meet this obligation."

FOR WHICH MUCH THANKS.

Sir: The Heraminer relates that James K. Hackett has refused to play the title rôle in "Mary, Queen of Scots." Gosh, but this is a relief! G. D. C.

THE SECOND POST.
[An order for a picture.]

Dear Sirs: I am sending you two photos and $5. I want you to have this work done as perfect as possible, there is a little alteration which I want made, which you will see as follows. Take the man from the single picture, which is my father, and paint him standing behind my mother which is setting in the chair on the grupe picture, or put him setting in another chair beside the girl on the same picture whichever you think will look the best to make a good picture, but I want the four persons in one big good picture. You will see that the picture has a redish flair, please try to get the others without any of that, also you will see that our eyes in the grupe picture is raised too high, please fix them looking natural, also put our eyebrows thick and natural, and make our faces as pleasant looking as possible, also you will notice in the picture that the girls dress is not sitting good from the waist down, please fix that setting smoothly as the breeze was blowing so hard in the yard that I could not keep my skirt setting in good shape around me, so please rectefy all these foults which I mention and make me a good picture as I want it to keep in memory of my family as we are now; you may put it in rich brown or sepia pastel whichever you think suits the picture the best, let the photoes be enlarged but full stature the same as the origenal.

A FIG FOR CEREMONY!

[From the East Peoria Post.]

New Year's Day our young friends, Miss Hattie Cochran and Mr. Elias King, without any ceremony at all were united in the bonds of holy wedlock.

THE SECOND POST.

[Received by the Chief of Police of Wichita, Kas.]

Der Sir: I am writing you to know if you have seen any thing of my wife in Wichita. She run off from me and a feller told me he seen her in Wichita having a big time. She is kinder Red Headed tolerable tall and has got a prety Bust in fact she is perfectly made up and you mite know of her by a Thing she has got tattooed on her rite thigh kindly in front of her leg. I think they aimed it for a Hart with L. M. in it but they kinder made a bum job of it and it is hard to make out what it is. If you here of her let me know it at wounced and I will come rite up fur her fur I want to See her bad. eny thing you let me no Surtenly will be appreciate. Yours truly, (Name on File).

P. S.—I may come rite to Wichita myself and see if I can find her, but you keep a look out fur her.

. . . What may interest you is that one of the Fords was owned by A. F. Fender.

OPEN THE GATES!

Sir: That sound of hoof-beats heralds the arrival, to join the Immortals, of Royal Ryder, a mounted copper in San Francisco.

G. Gray Shus.

[123]

THANKS to fifteen or twenty observant travelers for the info that the manager of the drug department of the Alexander Drug Co. in Omaha is George Salzgiver.

MISTER TOBIN, EDUCATOR.

A gentle, kindly man is he,
The soul of generosity;
Our little ones he gladly gives
The right to split infinitives.

The boys and girls who go to school
Approve of Mister Tobin's rule.
They find no cause to make complaint
At learning words like das't and ain't.

Two negatives has every boy,
And uses them with pride and joy·
And every girl has utmost skill
In interchanging shall and will.

Those noble boys and girls decry
The priggish use of "It is I."
If you should ask, "Who was with he?"
They'd answer simply, "It was me."

PANTALETTA.

IT IS not nice of readers to try to take advantage of our innocence. M. L. J., for example, writes out the valve-handle wheeze in longhand

and assures us that "it is an exact copy of a letter received by a stove manufacturing company in St. Louis, from a customer in Arkansas."

VARIANT OF THE VALVE-HANDLE WHEEZE.
(Received by a drug concern.)

GENTLEMEN: Your postal received, regarding an order which you sent us and which you have not, as yet, received.

Upon referring to our records, we fail to find any record of ever having received the order in question. The last order received from your firm was for a pair of flat cylindrical lenses to match broken sample you enclosed. This was taken care of the same day as received and sent on to you, properly addressed. We would suggest that you enter tracer with the postoffice department in endeavor to locate the package.

Regretting that it is necessary for us to give you this information, we remain, etc.

P. S. Since writing the above, the order in question was received at this office—this morning.

THE VALVE-HANDLE SNEEZE.

Sir: The handle on the valve is missing, and I can't turn off the radiator. The room was hot, and I've had to "open wide the windows, open wide the door." The resultant draft has just brought a series of "kerchoos" out of me. Valve-handle sneezes, I called them.   SIM NIC.

MISS EMILY DAVIS weds Mrs. Charles Parmele.—Wilmington, N. C., Dispatch.

Why don't the men propose, mama, why don't the men propose?

THE SANDS OF TIME.

Whenever I observe a quartette of commuters at cards I regret that the hours I gave to mastering whist were not given instead to the study of Greek.

"THE military salute," says our neighbor on the left, "is a courtesy of morale when it proceeds from one fighting man to another." This was impressed in 1918 upon a colored recruit who was hauled up for not saluting his s. o. His explanation was, "Ah thought you and me had got so well acquainted Ah didn't have to salute you no mo'."

THE TRUTH AT LAST!

Sir: Socrates and Epictetus did not learn Greek at 81—they were Greeks. It was the Roman Cato who began to study Greek at 80.

C. E. C.

Now that we all know it was neither Socrates nor Epictetus who learned Greek at 81 (because, you see, being Greeks they did not have to study the language), you may like to know something about Julius Cæsar. He was, narrates a high school paper, "the noblest of English kings. He learned Latin late in life in order to translate an ecclesiastical work into the vernaculary of the common people."

WE are reminded by our learned friend, W. F. Y., that Socrates began at 64 to study English, but had to give it up as a bad job. "The fact," he says, "is interestingly set forth in Montefiori's 'Eccentricities of Genius.'"

THE attitude of our universities and other quasi-educational institutions toward Greek is that 81 is the proper age for beginning the study of it.

BREATHING defiance of the Eighteenth Amendment, Jay Rye and Jewel Bacchus were married in Russellville, Ark., last Sunday.

THE Wetmore Shop, on Belmont avenue, advertises "Everything for the baby."

Sir: I feel that the time has come to call your attention to a letter received from C. A. Neuenhahn, of St. Louis. It concludes CAN/IT.

A. E. W.

PERSONS who cannot compose 200 words of correct and smooth running English will write to a newspaper to criticize a "long and labored editorial." A labored editorial is one with which a reader does not agree.

THINK OF IT!

Take any life you choose and study it.
Take Edgar Lee Masters':
He is a lawyer and a poet;
Or perhaps it is best to call him
A lawyer-poet,
Or a poet who was never much at law,
Or t'other way around if you prefer.
Whichever way 'tis put, the fact remains
He wrote a poem that now sells
For fifty cents plus four beans.

Think of it!
Four dollars and fifty cents,
Or, if you prefer,
$4.50.
And Elenor Murray did not have a cent on her
When they found her body on the banks
Of the Squeehunk river.

And the poem is out of stock at half the stores.
And Villon starved and Keats, Keats—
Where am I? I don't know.

YSEULT POTTS.

[128]

THE headline, "U. S. to Seize Wet Doctors," has led many readers to wonder whether the government will get after the nurses next.

WE have always been in sympathy with President Wilson's idea of democracy. He expressed it perfectly when he was president of Princeton. "Unless I have entire power," said he, "how can I make this a democratic college?"

THE complete skeptic is skeptical about skepticism; and there is one day in the round of days, this one, when he may lay aside his glasses, faintly tinted blue, and put on instead, not the rose-colored specs of Dr. Pangloss, but a glass that blurs somewhat the outlines of men and things; and these he may wear until midnight. The only objects which this glass does not blur are children. Seen through blue, or rose, or white, children are always the same. They have not changed since Bethlehem.

A VERY good motto for any family is that which the Keiths of Scotland selected a-many years ago: "They say. What say they? Let them say." It might even do for the top of this Totem-Pole of Tooralay.

A FREQUENT question since the war began is, "Why are there so many damn fools in the faculties of American universities?" Chancellor Williams of Wooster turns light on the mystery. Eminent educators who are also damn fools are hypermorons, who are intellectual but not truly intelligent. He says of these queer beings:

"The hypermoron may laugh in imitation of others, but he has no original humor and very little original wit. The cause for this is that original wit and humor require unusual combinations of factors; but the very nature of the hypermoron is that he does not arrange and perceive such combinations. When the hypermoron does cause laughter from some speech or action, usually he resents it. But when a normal man unconsciously does or says something laughable, he himself shares in making sport of himself. Though at times amiable, the hypermoron invariably takes himself so seriously as in a long acquaintance to become tiresome."

THE ENRAPTURED SOCIETY EDITOR.

[From the Charlotte, Ky., Chronicle.]

The lovely and elegant home of that crown prince of hospitality, the big hearted and noble souled Ab. Weaver, was a radiant scene of enchanting loveliness, for Cupid had brought one of his finest offerings to the court of Hymen, for the lovable Miss Maude, the beautiful daughter of Mr. Weaver and his refined and most excellent wife, who is a lady of rarest charms and sweetest graces, dedicated her life's ministry to Dr. James E. Hobgood, the brilliant and gifted and talented son of that ripe scholar and renowned educator, the learned Prof. Hobgood, the very able and successful president of the Oxford Female college.

THE MISCHIEVOUS MAKE-UP MAN.
[From the Markesan, Wis., Herald.]

It is a wise man who knows when he has made a fool of himself.

A baby boy was born to Mr. and Mrs. Emil Zimmerman of Mackford yesterday.

WHY THE MAKE-UP MAN LEFT TOWN.
[From the Grinnell Review.]

Born, April 19, to Professor and Mrs. J. P. Ryan, a daughter.

This experience suggests that simple scientific experiments performed by college students would furnish a very interesting program of entertainment in any community.

COOL, INDEED!
[From the Tuttle, N. D., Star.]

At the burning of a barn in Steele recently, our superintendent displayed some nerve and pluck. Miss Sherman did not wait for the men to get there but hastened to the barn without stopping

[131]

to dress, and in bare feet untied the horses before they had become unmanageable thus saving
them with little trouble.   There is not a man, we
venture to say, in all Steele but would have
stopped to put on his pants before venturing out
into the crisp air, but she did not, her whole
thought being of the dumb animals imperiled, and
it was, indeed, a nervy and cool-headed performance.

RHYMED DEVOTION.

[Robert Louis Stevenson to his wife.]

When my wife is far from me
The undersigned feels all at sea.
R. L. S.

I was as good as deaf
When separate from F.

I am far from gay
When separate from A.

I loathe the ways of men
When separate from N.

Life is a murky den
When separate from N.

My sorrow rages high
When separate from Y.

And all things seem uncanny
When separate from Fanny.

[132]

LACKING the equipment of the monk in Daudet's tale, an amateur distiller is gauging his output with an instrument used for testing the fluid in his motor car's radiator. "Yesterday," reports P. D. P., "he confided to me that he had some thirty below zero stuff."

FISH talk to each other, Dr. Bell tells the Geographic society; a statement which no one will doubt who has ever seen a pair of goldfish in earnest conversation.

ACCORDING to Dr. Eliot, Americans are more and more becoming subject to herd impulses, gregarious impulses, common emotions, and he is considerably annoyed. Heaven be praised if what he says be true! He would have individuality released; which is precisely what we do not want. Americans are not individuals, and they are not free; but they think they are. Therefore is America, in these troublous times, an island in chaos, where civilization, like Custer, will make its last stand.

DOCTORS disagree as to whether 70 degrees is the proper temperature for an apartment. This will intrigue a friend of ours who, preferring 60 degrees himself, is obliged to maintain a temperature of almost 80 because of his mother-in-law.

"WOMEN," says Dr. Ethel Smyth, of London (perhaps you know Ethel), "women have undoubtedly invaluable work to do as composers." Quite so. And any time they are ready to begin we'll sit up and take notice.

SH-H-H! On Main street in Buffalo, near the Hotel Iroquois, you can have "Tattooing Done Privately Inside."

SHALL we not revise Shakespeare:
 The chariest maid is prodigal enough
 If she unmask her beauty on the Boul.

A NEW FIRM IN FISH.
[From the Kearney Neb., Democrat.]

Fresh Smoked Finn & Haddies at Keller's Market.

OUR interest in baseball has waned, but we still can watch workmen on a skyscraper throwing and catching red-hot rivets.

THE dinosaur, having two sets of brains (as we once pointed out in imperishable verse), was able to reason *a priori* and *a posteriori* with equal facility. But what we started to mention was an ad in the American Lumberman calling for "a good all around yellow pine office man of broad wholesale experience, well posted on both ends."

AMONG the new publications of Richard G. Badger we lamp, "Nervous Children: Their Prevention and Management."

UNRELIEVED pessimism rather shocks us. In spite of everything we are willing to look on the bright side. We are willing to agree that, in some previous incarnation, we may have inhabited a crookeder world than this.

THE valued News, of New York, dismisses lightly the fear that the Puritan Sabbath will be restored. Ten or twenty years ago people dismissed as lightly the fear that Prohibition would be saddled on the country. On his way to the compulsory Wednesday-evening prayer meeting, a few years hence, the editor of the News will recall his cheerful and baseless prediction in 1920.

FIRED by liquor, men maltreat their wives. These wretches deserve public flogging; hanging were a compliment to some of them. On the other hand, men made emotional by liquor have conceived an extravagant fondness for their wives. We have not read about liquor floating the matrimonial bark over the shallows of domestic discord; yet men who have fared homeward with unsteady footsteps under the blinking stars, know that in such moments they are much more humane than in sober daylight; they are appalled by their own unworthiness, and thinking of their wives moves them almost to tears—quite, not infrequently. They resolve to become better husbands and fathers. The spirit of the wine in them captains "an army of shining and generous dreams," an army that is easily routed, an army that the wife too often puts to flight with an injudicious criticism. It is said that since Prohibition came in the cases of cruelty to wives have increased greatly in number. We do not disbelieve this. Bluebeard was a dry.

WHAT DO YOU SUPPOSE HE WANTS?
[Received by Farm Mechanics.]

Gentlemen: Will you please send me a specimen copy of the Farm Mechanics. I would like a sample of the Farm Mechanics very much. I sincerely trust that you will mail me a sample copy of Farm Mechanics as I want to see a specimen of your Farm Mechanics very much. Yours very truly, etc.

ALTHOUGH Mrs. Elizabeth Hash has retired from the hotel business, Mrs. Peter Lunch has undertaken to manage the Metropole cafeteria in Fargo, N. D.

Sioux Falls

[From the Sioux Falls Press.]

What if we don't have palaces, 5
With damp and musty walls?
We have the great Sioux River,
And greater yet, Sioux Falls.

We don't have to go abroad,
God's beauties just to see,
But stay at home
And take a trip
Around Sioux Falls with me.

WE confess a fondness for verse like the foregoing, and hope some day to find a poem as good
as that masterpiece—

"I've traveled east, I've traveled west,
I've been to the great Montana,
But the finest place I've ever seen
Is Attica, Indiana."

ANOTHER popular pome of sentiment and reflection, heard by L. M. G. in Wisconsin lumber
camps, is—

"I've traveled east, I've traveled west,
As far as the town of Fargo,
But the darndest town I ever struck
Is the town they call Chicargo."

[137]

"USELESS VERBIAGE."

[From an abstract of title.]

"That said Mary Ann Wolcott died an infant, 2 or 3 years old, unmarried, intestate, and that she left no husband, child, or children."

INGENIOUS CALIFORNIA PARADOX.

[From the Oakland Post.]

The Six-Minute Ferry route across the bay will take only eighteen to twenty minutes.

ALMOST.

Sir: S. Fein has put his name on the door of his orange-colored taxicab. Can you whittle a wheeze out of that?   R. A. J.

KNUT HAMSUN, winner of the Nobel prize for literature, used to be a street-car conductor in Chicago. This is a hint to column conductors. Get a transfer.

The Witch's Holiday.

A TALE FOR CHILDREN ONLY.

I.

MATTERS had gone ill all the day; and, to cap what is learnedly called the perverseness of inanimate things, it came on to rain just as the Boy, having finished his lessons, was on the point of setting out for a romp in the brown fields.

"Isn't it perfectly mean, Mowgli?" he complained to his dog. The water spaniel wagged a noncommittal tail and stretched himself before the wood fire with a deep drawn sigh. The rain promised to hold, so the Boy took down a book and curled up in a big leather chair.

It was a very interesting book—all about American pioneers, trappers, and Indians; and although the writer of it was a German traveler, no American woodsman would take advantage of a worthy German globe trotter and tell him things which were not exactly so. For example, if you and a trapper and a dog were gathered about a campfire, and the dog were asleep and dreaming in his sleep, and the trapper should affirm that if you tied a handkerchief over the head of a dreaming dog and afterwards tied it around your own head, you would have the dog's dream,—if the trapper should tell you this with

[139]

a perfectly serious face, you naturally would believe him, especially if you were a German traveler.

The Boy got up softly and began the experiment. Mowgli opened an inquiring eye, stretched himself another notch, and fell asleep again. His master waited five minutes, then unloosed the handkerchief and knotted it under his own chin.

For a while Mowgli's slumbers were untroubled as a forest pool, his breathing as regular as the tick-tock of the old wooden clock under the stair. Out of doors the rain fell sharply and set the dead leaves singing. The wood fire dwindled to a glow. Tick-tock! tick-tock! drummed the ancient timepiece. The Boy yawned and settled deeper in the leather chair.

Tick-tock! Tick-tock!

Mowgli was breathing out of time. He was twitching, and making funny little smothered noises, which, if he were awake, would probably be yelps. Something exciting was going on in dreamland.

Tick-tock! Tick——

HULLO! There goes a woodchuck!

II.

The Boy gave chase across the fields, only to arrive, out of breath, at the entrance to a burrow down which the woodchuck had tumbled.

He had not a notion where he was. He seemed to have raced out of the world that he knew into one which was quite unfamiliar. It was a broad valley inclosed by high hills, through which a pleasant little river ran; and the landscape wore an odd aspect—the hills were bluer than hills usually are, the trees were more fantastically fashioned, and the waving grass and flowers were more beautiful than one commonly sees.

"Good morning, young sir!"

On the other side of the stream stood a tall man wrapped in a cloak and leaning with both hands upon a staff. He was well past the middle years, as wrinkles and a beard turned gray gave evidence; but his eyes were youthful and his cheeks as ruddy as a farm lad's. His clothing was worn and dust-laden, but of good quality and unpatched, and there was an air about him that said plainly, "Here is no common person, I can tell you."

"You are wondering who I may be," he observed. "Well, then, I am known as the Knight of the Dusty Thoroughfare."

"A queer sort of knight, this!" thought the Boy.

"And you—may I ask whither you are bound?" said the stranger. "We may be traveling the same road."

The Boy made answer that he had set forth

to chase a woodchuck, and that having failed to catch it he had no better plan than to return home.

At the word "home" the Knight put on a melancholy smile, and cutting a reed at the river edge he fashioned it into a pipe and began to play. A wonderful tune it was. Tom the Piper's Son knew the way of it, and to the same swinging melody the Pied Piper footed the streets of Hamelin town; for the burden of the tune was "Over the Hills and Far Away," and the Boy's feet stirred at the catch of it.

"That," said the Knight, "is the tune I have marched to for many a year, and a pretty chase it has led me." He put down the pipe. "Knocking about aimlessly does very well for an old man, but youth should have a definite goal."

The Boy did not agree with this. With that magic melody marching in his head it was hey for the hills and the westering sun, and the pleasant road to Anywhere.

"What lies yonder?" he queried, pointing to a deep notch in the skyline.

"The Kingdom of Rainbow's End," replied the Knight. It is an agreeable territory, and you would do very well to journey thither. The King of the country is no longer young, and as he has nothing to say about affairs of state, or anything else for that matter, he spends his time tramping about from place to place, in much the same fashion as myself."

"And who governs while he is away?"

"SHE!" said the Knight solemnly—"SHE THAT BOSSES EVERYBODY!"

III.

"You see," said the Knight of the Dusty Thoroughfare, "the King made a grave mistake some years ago. It is a foolish saying that when a man marries his troubles begin; but it is the law of Rainbow's-End that when a man marries he may chloroform his mother-in-law or not, just as he pleases. But if he forfeit the right he may never again claim it, and the deuce take him for a softhearted simpleton."

The Boy thought it a barbarous law and so declared.

"There is something to be said for it," returned the Knight. A mother-in-law is like the little girl with the little curl. It so happens that the King's mother-in-law is a very unpleasant old party, and the King made a sad mess of it when he threw the chloroform bottle out of the window."

"Tell me about Rainbow's-End," the Boy entreated. "Is there a beautiful Princess, with many suitors for her hand?"

"The Princess Aralia is a very pretty girl, as

[143]

princesses go." The Knight opened a locket attached to a long gold chain and exhibited an exquisite miniature. "I don't mind saying," said he, "that the Princess Aralia and I are on very good terms, and a word from me will procure you a cordial reception. The question is, how shall we set about it? You can't present yourself at court as you are; you must have a horse and a fine costume, and all that sort of thing."

"Perhaps there's a good fairy in the neighborhood," said the Boy hopefully.

The Knight shook his head. "Not within a dozen leagues. But stop a bit—it is just possible that Aunt Jo can manage the matter. Aunt Jo is the sister of my wife's mother, and one of the cleverest witches in the country. She stands very high in her profession and is thoroughly schooled in every branch of deviltry; and with the exception of my wife's mother, I can think of no person whose society is less desirable. But one day in each year she takes a day off, during which she is as affable and benevolent an old dame as you can possibly imagine; really, you would never know it was the same person. These annual breathing spells do her a world of good, she tells me; for incessant wickedness is just as monotonous and wearisome as unbroken goodness."

"And to-day is the Witch's holiday?"

"Yes, it so happens; and I always make it a

[144]

point to spend the night at her cottage if I am in this part of the country."

The Knight of the Dusty Thoroughfare rose and put his cloak about his shoulders, and with the Boy set forward through the valley.

IV.

Presently they came to the Witch's cottage, snuggled away in a hollow and hidden from the road by a tangle of witch hazel shrubs. The Boy rather expected a dark, forbidding hut of sinister outlines, but here was as pretty a cabin as ever you saw, weathered a pleasing gray, with green blinds and a tiny porch overrun with Virginia-creeper.

The Knight strode boldly up the path, the Boy following less confidently. No one answering the summons at the porch, they tried the kitchen door. It was open, and they stepped inside. The Witch was not at home, but evidently she was not far away, for a fire was crackling in the stove and a kettle singing over the flames. An enormous black cat got up lazily from the hearth and rubbed himself against the visitors with a purr like a small dynamo.

With the familiarity of a relative the Knight led the way about the house. One door was locked. "This," said he, "is Aunt Jo's dark room, in which she develops her deviltry. This"—opening the door of a little shed—"is the garage."

The Boy peeped in and saw two autobroom-sticks.

"The small green one is her runabout. The big red one is a touring broomstick, high power and very fast; you can hear her coming a mile off."

They returned to the sitting room, and the Boy became greatly taken with Aunt Jo's collection of books. Some of these were: "One Hundred and One Best Broths," "Witchcraft Self-Taught," "The Black Art—Berlitz Method," and "Burbank's Complete Wizard." The Boy took down the "Complete Wizard," but he was not able to do more than glance at the absorbing contents before the clicking of the gate announced that the Witch had returned.

Aunt Jo was a sprightly dame of more than seventy years, very thin, but straight and supple, and with hair still jet black. Her eyes were gray-green or green-gray, as the light happened to strike them; her cheeks were hollow, and a long sharp chin slanted up to meet a long sharp nose. Ordinarily, as the Knight had hinted, she was no doubt an unholy terror, but to-day she was in the best of humors, and her eyes twinkled with good nature.

"I just stepped out," she explained, "to carry some jelly and cake to one of my neighbors, a woodcutter's wife. The poor woman has been ill all the summer! Mercy! if I haven't had a

[146]

day of it!" She dropped into a chair, brushing a fly from the tip of her nose with the tip of her tongue. "How is everything in Rainbow's-End?" she asked. "I suppose SHE is as bad as ever."

"Worse," replied the Knight, fetching a sigh. "And SHE never takes a day off, as you do."

"Well, Henry, it's your own fault, as I've told you a thousand times. If you hadn't been so soft-hearted—— But mercy! that's no way to be talking on my holiday."

"So!" said the Boy to himself. "This wandering knight is the King of Rainbow's-End and the father of the Princess. I have a friend at court indeed."

V.

"And how is the Princess Aralia?" asked the Witch. "As pretty as ever, I suppose, and with no prospect of a husband, thanks to her grandmother and the silly tasks she sets for the suitors."

"That brings us to the business of our young friend here," said the Knight of the Dusty Thoroughfare. "He wishes to present himself at court, and is in great need of a horse and wardrobe."

"You've come to the wrong shop for horses and fine feathers," said the Witch. "Those things are quite out of my line."

The Boy looked his disappointment.

[147]

"The best I can do," said Aunt Jo kindly, "is to give you a letter to a Mr. Burbank, an excellent wizard of my acquaintance. He has recently invented a skinless grape and a watermelon that is all heart, and is quite the cleverest man in the business. Such a trifle as changing a pig into a horse will give him no trouble whatever. Have you seen my garden, Henry?"

"No, but I should like to," said the Knight rising.

"Meanwhile," said the Witch, "I will start the supper if our young friend will fetch the wood."

The Boy responded with such cheerful readiness that Aunt Jo patted him on the cheek and said: "You're the lad for the Princess Aralia, and have her you shall if Aunt Jo can bring it about. And now go out in the garden and pick me a hatful of Brussels sprouts."

It was impossible to imagine a more appetizing supper than that which the three sat down to. Everything was prepared to a nicety, and the Knight could not say enough in praise of the raised biscuits and home made currant jell. As for the doughnuts, "Such doughnuts can't be made without witchcraft, Jo," he declared.

"Nonsense!" said the old lady. "I don't put a thing into them that any good cook doesn't use. Making doughnuts always was an art by itself. You must both take some with you when you go."

After supper the Knight wiped the dishes while the Witch washed them, Aunt Jo declaring it a shame that a man so domestically inclined should be compelled to wander from one end of the rainbow to the other just because of a foolish tenderheartedness in days gone by. While the pair discussed this fruitful topic the Boy dipped into the fascinating chapters of the "Complete Wizard."

"Time for bed," announced the Knight an hour later; and he added for the Boy's ear: "We must make an early start in the morning."

"I for one shall sleep soundly," Aunt Jo declared. "I've run my legs off to-day, as I never use a broomstick on my holiday."

She conducted her guests to a tiny bedchamber above stairs. "I will leave a bag of doughnuts on the table, Henry," said she, "as I suppose you will be off before I am up. Good-night!"

When she had gone below the Knight said: "We must be moving with the first streak of day. Aunt Jo's holiday ends with sun-up, and you would find her a vastly different old party, I can tell you."

VI.

"I don't think I should be afraid of her," said the Boy.

The Knight chuckled, and without further speech got into bed and was soon wrapped in a deep slumber. Next to a clear conscience and the open road, a good bed at night is something to set store by.

But the Boy could not sleep for the exciting pictures that danced in his head, and he was impatient for the morning light, that he might be on his way to Rainbow's-End. The moon peeped in the window; the breeze made a pleasant sound in the poplar trees; from somewhere came the music of a little brook. To all these gentle influences the Boy finally yielded.

He was awakened by a plucking at his sleeve.

"Time to be moving," said the Knight in a hoarse whisper. "We can put on our shoes after we leave the house."

They crept down the stair, which creaked in terrifying fashion, but a gentle snoring from the Witch's bedroom reassured them. After they had tiptoed out of the house and gained the road they discovered that they had forgotten the bag of doughnuts. The Knight declared that he would not return for a million doughnuts, but the Boy, remembering how delicious they tasted, stole back to the door and lifted the latch softly. Aunt Jo was still snoring, but, just as he laid hold of the doughnuts, Pluto the cat came leaping in from the kitchen, and the Boy had barely time to put the door between its sharp claws and himself. He ran down the path, vaulted the gate, and looked about for the Knight. Away down the road was a rapidly diminishing figure.

The Boy was a good runner, and he was fast overtaking the Knight, when the latter, who had been casting anxious glances over his shoulder as he ran, suddenly plunged into the bushes at one side of the road. The Boy thought it wise to follow his example.

And not a moment too soon. A small whirring sound grew louder and louder, and Aunt Jo went whizzing by on her high power autobroomstick, leaving in her wake a horrible reek of gasoline and brimstone. But not the Aunt Jo of the evening before. Her green eyes flashed behind the goggles, and her face was something dreadful to behold. On her shoulder perched Pluto, every hair erect, and spitting fire.

The Boy gasped, and hoped he had seen the last of the terrible hag, when the whirring noise announced that she was coming back. She stopped her broomstick directly opposite the hiding-place and began cutting small circles in the air, the while peering sharply about.

As the Boy plunged into the thicket, he fell. As he lay there, something cold pressed against his hand.

It was Mowgli's nose. The dog's eyes questioned his master, who had cried out in his sleep.

"Oh, Mowgli!" he exclaimed, taking the spaniel by his shaggy ears, "did you dream *all* that wonderful dream? Or did you stop at the wood-chuck hole? What a shame, Mowgli, if there shouldn't really be a Knight of the Dusty Thoroughfare, and a Princess Aralia and a Witch who makes wonderful doughnuts!"

A LINE-O'-TYPE OR TWO

"Nous ne trouvons guère de gens de bon sens que ceux qui sont de notre avis."
—*La Rochefoucauld.*

"THE FRIEND OF THE PEOPLE."

Old Amicus Pop
Is the friend of the Wop,
The friend of the Chink and the Harp,
The friend of all nations
And folk of all stations,
The friend of the shark and the carp.
He sits in his chair
With his feet on the table,
And lists to the prayer
Of Minerva and Mabel,
Veritas, Pro Bono, Taxpayer, and the rest,
Who wail on his shoulder and weep on his breast.

Old Amicus Pop
Is the solace and prop
Of all who are weary of life.
He straightens the tangles
And jangles and wrangles
That breed in this city of strife.
Whatever your "beef,"
You may pour him an earful;

[153]

Unbottle your grief
        Be it ever so tearful.
Oh, weep all you wish—he is there with the mop.
Bring all of your troubles to Amicus Pop.

WHEN we think of the countless thousands who peruse this Cro'-nest of Criticism, a feeling of responsibility weighs heavily upon us, and almost spoils our day. Frezzample, one writes from St. Paul: "We have twenty confirmed readers of the Line in this 'house.'" The quotation marks disturb us. Can it be a sanitarium?

MOST of the trouble in this world is caused by people who do not know when they are well off. The Germans did not know when they were well off. Your cook, who left last week, as little apprehended her good fortune. Nor will the Filipinos be happy till they get it.

THOSE who stand in awe of persons with logical minds will be reassured by Henry Adams' pertinent reflection that the mind resorts to reason for want of training. His definition of philosophy is also reassuring: "Unintelligible answers to insoluble problems."

AMONG those who have guessed at the meaning of "the freedom of the seas" was Cowper:

"Without one friend, above all foes,
    Britannia gives the world repose."

[154]

MAXWELL BODENHEIM has published a book of poems, and the critics allow that Max Boden's brays are bonnie.

IF YOU MUST KISS, KISS THE DOCTOR.
[From "How to Avoid Influenza."]

Avoid kissing, as this habit readily transmits influenza. If physician is available, it is best to consult him.

QUICK, WATSON, THE PLUMBER!
[From the Cedar Rapids Gazette.]

Mrs. T. M. Dripps gave a dinner Friday in honor of Mrs. D. L. Leek of South Dakota.

"KIND Captain, I've important information." Mr. Honkavaarra runs an automobile livery in Palmer, Mich.

"THE first child, Lord Blandford, was born in 1907; the second was born in 1898."—Chicago American.
This so annoyed the Duke, that a reconciliation was never possible.

WHEN your friend points with pride to a picture that, in your judgment, leaves something to be desired, or when he exhibits the latest addition to his family, you may be perplexed to voice an

opinion that will satisfy both him and your con-
science. An artist friend of ours is never at a loss.
If it is a picture, he exclaims, "Extraordinary!"
If it is an infant, he remarks, *"There is a baby!"*
He might add, with the English wit. "one more
easily conceived than described."

THE advantages of a classical education are so
obvious that the present-day battle in its behalf
seems a waste of energy. Frezzample, without a
classical education how could you appreciate the
fact that Mr. Odessey is now running a Noah's
Ark candy kitchen in St. Peter, Wis.?

ONE may believe that the "gift of healing" is
nothing more than the application of imaginary
balm to non-existent disease, but if one says so
he gets into a jolly row with people who consider
an open mind synonymous with credulity. Our
own state of mind was accurately described by
Charles A. Dana: "I don't believe in ghosts,"
said he, "but I've been afraid of them all my life."

THE congregation will rise and sing:
Bill Bryan's heart is a-mouldering in the grave,
But his lungs go marching on.

THE astronomer Hamilton "made an expedition to Dublin to substitute a semi-colon for a
colon"; but, reports J. E. R., "my wife's brother's

brother-in-law's doctor charged him $600 for removing only part of a colon."

FEW readers realize how much time is expended in making certain that commas are properly distributed. Thomas Campbell walked six miles to a printer's to have a comma in one of his poems changed to a semi-colon.

FOLLOWING a bout with the gloves, a Seattle clubman is reported "in a state of comma." A doctor writes us that infection by the colon bacillus can be excluded, but we should say that what the patient needs is not a doctor but a proof reader.

"SHE played Liszt's Rhapsodie No. 2 with remarkable speed," relates the Indianapolis News. In disposing of Liszt's Rhapsodies it is all right to step on the accelerator, as the sooner they are finished the better.

GIVE US THIS DAY OUR DAILY CLIMATE,
AND FORGIVE US OUR DROPS IN
TEMPERATURE!
[From the Pasadena Star-News.]

To put it in another form of expression, Mother Nature maintains poise and evenness of temper in this state far better than in most regions on this terrestrial ball. If you haven't thanked

[157]

God to-day that you are privileged to live in California it is not yet too late to do so. Make it a daily habit. The blessing is worth this frequent expression of gratitude to the All High.

VARIANT OF A MORE OR LESS WELL KNOWN STORY.

[From the Exeter, Neb., News.]

Whoever took the whole pumpkin pie from Mrs. W. H. Taylor's kitchen the night of the party was welcome to it as the cat had stepped in it twice and it could not be used. Many thanks for the pan, she says.

THE WORLD'S GREATEST WINTER RESORT.

"Because of high temperatures and chinooks Medicine Hat is menaced with an ice famine."

They bask in the sunshine and purr like a cat,
The fortunate people of Medicine Hat.

Its climate is balmy in spite of the lat.;
You have a wrong notion of Medicine Hat.

At Christmas they sit on their porches and chat,
For it never gets chilly in Medicine Hat.

The Medicine Hatters all spoil for a spat
With any defamer of Medicine Hat;

They're ready and anxious to go to the mat
With any one scoffing at Medicine Hat.

[158]

The birds never migrate—they know where they're at,
For it always is summer in Medicine Hat.

No day that you can't use a heliostat;
Sunlight is eternal in Medicine Hat.

They're swatting the fly and the skeeter and gnat,
As frost never kills them in Medicine Hat.

His nature is skeptic, he's blind as a bat
Who can't see the beauties of Medicine Hat.

All jesting is flatulent, futile, and flat
That libels the climate of Medicine Hat.

Away with the knockers who knock it, and drat
The jokers who joke about Medicine Hat.

In short, it's the one, the ideal habitat.
Boy! buy me a ticket to Medicine Hat!

ACCORDING to the Milford Herald a young couple were married "under the strain of Mendelssohn's wedding march."

THE VILLAGE OMAR LOSES HIS OUTFIT.
[From the Fort Dodge Messenger.]

Lost—Grass rug and ukulele between Shady Oaks and Fort Dodge. Finder notify Messenger.

"THELANDER-ECKBLADE Wedding Solomonized," reports the Batavia Herald. Interesting and unusual.

[159]

"TWEET! TWEET!" GOES THE ENRAP-
TURED REPORTER.

[From the Sterling Gazette.]

The wedding party wended its way to the grove
south of the river and there, in a lovely spot,
where pleasant hours of courtship have been
passed, the wedding ceremony was performed.
No stately church edifice built by man, no gilded
altar, no polished pews nor polished floors were
there; no stately organ or trained choir; there
was an absence of ushers, bridesmaids and par-
son heavily gowned. No curious crowd thronged
without the portal. In place of this display and
grandeur they were surrounded by an edifice of
nature's planting—the stately forest tree, while
the green sward of the verdant grove furnished
a velvety carpet. There, in this beautiful spot,
where the Creator ordained such events to occur,
the young couple, true lovers of the simple life,
took upon themselves the vows which united them
until "death itself should part." The rustle of
the leaves in the treetop murmured nature's sweet
benediction, while the bluebird, the robin, and the
thrush sang a glorious doxology.

WEDDED, in Clay county, Illinois, Emma Pickle
and Gay Gerking. A wedding gift from Mr.
Heinz or Squire Dingee would not be amiss.

A SPLENDID RECOVERY.

[Waukesha, Wis., item.]

Mr. and Mrs. J. Earl Stallard are the proud parents of an eight pound boy, born at the Municipal hospital this morning. Mr. Stallard will be able to resume his duties as county agricultural agent by to-morrow.

HOW FAST THE LEAVES ARE FALLING!

[From the Waterloo Courier.]

Frank Fuller, night operator at the Illinois Central telegraph office, has been kept more than busy to-day, all because of a ten pound boy who arrived at his home last evening. Mr. Fuller has decided that he will spend all of his evenings at his home in the future.

HOW SOON IT GETS DARK THESE DAYS!

[From the Pillager, Minn., Herald.]

That stork is a busy bird. It left a 10-lb baby girl at Ned Mickles last Thursday night. Ned is a neighbor of Cy Deaver.

UPON JULIA'S ARCTICS.

Whenas galoshed my Julia goes,
Unbuckled all from top to toes,
How swift the poem becometh prose!
And when I cast mine eyes and see
Those arctics flopping each way free,
Oh, how that flopping floppeth me!

[161]

"We are all in the dark together," says Anatole France; "the only difference is, the savant keeps knocking at the wall, while the ignoramus stays quietly in the middle of the room." We used to be intensely interested in the knocking of the savants, but as nothing ever came of it, we have become satisfied with the middle of the room.

A GOOD MOTTO.

I was conversing with Mr. Carlton the Librarian, and he quoted from memory a line from Catulle Mendès that seemed to me uncommonly felicitous: "La vie est un jour de Mi-Carême. Quelques-uns se masquent; moi, je ris."

In his declining years M. France has associated himself with the bunch called "Clarté," a conscious group organized by Barbusse, the object of which is the "union of all partisans of the true right and the true liberty." . How wittily the Abbé Coignard would have discussed "Clarté," and how wisely M. Bergeret would have considered it! Alas! it is sad to lose one's hair, but it is a tragedy to lose one's unbeliefs.

Chicago, as has been intimated, rather broadly, is a jay town; but it is coming on. A department store advertises "cigarette cases and holders for the gay sub-deb and her great-grand-mother," also "a diary for 'her' if she leads an exciting life."

WE infer from the reviews of John Burroughs' "Accepting the Universe" that John has decided to accept it. One might as well. With the reservation that acceptance does not imply approval.

IT is possible that Schopenhauer wrote his w. k. essay on woman after a visit to a bathing beach.

WE heard a good definition of a bore. A bore is a man who, when you ask him how he is, tells you.

THE sleeping sickness (not the African variety) is more mysterious than the flu. It will be remembered that two things were discovered about the flu: first, that it was caused by a certain bacillus, and, second, that it was not caused by that bacillus. But all that is known about the sleeping sickness is that it attacks, by preference, carpenters and plumbers.

SLANGY and prophetic Mérimée, who wrote, in "Love Letters of a Genius": "You may take it from me that . . . short dresses will be the order of the day, and those who are blessed with natural advantages will be at last distinguished from those whose advantages are artificial only."

HAPPY above all other writing mortals we esteem him who, like Barrie, treads with sure feet the borderland 'twixt fact and faery, stepping now on this side, now on that. One must write with moist eyes many pages of such a fantasy as "A Kiss for Cinderella." There are tears that are not laughter's, nor grief's, but beauty's own. A lovely landscape may bring them, or a strain of music, or a written or a spoken line.

ALL we can get out of a Shaw play is two hours and a half of mental exhilaration. We are, inscrutably, denied the pleasure of wondering what Shaw means, or whether he is sincere.

WHY THE MAKE-UP FLED.
[From the Dodge Center Record.]

Mr. and Mrs. Umberhocker returned yesterday from an over Sunday visit with their son and family in Minneapolis.

They are in hopes to soon land them in jail as they did the hog thieves, who were to have a hearing but waved it and trial will be held later.

"IT isn't hard to sit up with a sick friend when he has a charming sister," reports B. B. But if it were a sick horse, Venus herself would be in the way.

[164]

"SAVING the penny is all right," writes a vox-popper to the Menominee News, "but saving the dollar is 100 per cent better." At least.

MUSIC HATH CHAHMS.

What opus of Brahms' is your pet?—
A concerto, a trio, duet,
Sonate No. 3
(For Viol. and P.),
Or the second piano quartette?

SARDI.

Our favorite Brahms? We're not sûr,
For all are so classique et pur;
But we'll mention an opus
With which you may dope us—
One Hundred and Sixteen, E dur.

BRAHMS, OPUS 116.

I care for your pet, One Sixteen
(Your choice proves your judgment is keen);
 But in E, you forget, see,
 It has two intermezzi;
Please, which of these twain do you mean?

SARDI.

Which E? Can you ask? Must we tell?
Doth it not every other excel—
 The ineffable one,
 Of gossamer spun,
The ultimate spirituelle.

A CANDID butcher in Battle Creek advertises "Terrible cuts."

ANOTHER candid merchant in Ottumwa, Ia., advises: "Buy to-day and think to-morrow."

MUSIC HINT.

Sir: P. A. Scholes, in his "Listener's Guide to Music," revives two good laughs—thus: "A fugue is a piece in which the voices one by one come in and the people one by one go out." Also he quotes from Sam'l Butler's Note Books: "I pleased Jones by saying that the hautbois was a clarinet with a cold in its head, and the bassoon the same with a cold in its chest." The cor anglais suffers slightly from both symptoms. Some ambitious composer, by judicious use of the more diseased instruments, could achieve the most rheumy musical effects, particularly if, à la Scriabin, he should have the atmosphere of the concert hall heavily charged with eucalyptus.

E. PONTIFEX.

"I WILL now sing for you," announced a contralto to a woman's club meeting in the Copley-Plaza, "a composition by one of Boston's noted composers, Mr. Chadwick. 'He loves me.'" And of course everybody thought George wrote it for *her*.

"GRAND opera is, above all others, the high-brow form of entertainment."—Chicago Journal.
Yes. In comparison, a concert of chamber music appears trifling and almost vulgar.

AT a reception in San Francisco, Mrs. Wandazetta Fuller-Biers sang and Mrs. Mabel Boone-Sooey read. Cannot they be signed for an entertainment in the Academy?

WE simply cannot understand why Dorothy Pound, pianist, and Isabelle Bellows, singer, of the American Conservatory, do not hitch up for a concert tour.

RICHARD STRAUSS has been defined as a musician who was once a genius. Now comes another felicitous definition—"Unitarian: a Retired Christian."

DR. HYSLOP, the psychical research man, says that the spirit world is full of cranks. These, we take it, are not on the spirit level.

THE present physical training instructor in the Waterloo, Ia., Y. W. C. A. is Miss Armstrong. Paradoxically, the position was formerly held by Miss Goodenough. These things appear to interest many readers.

[167]

THE HUNTING OF THE PACIFIST SNARK.
(With Mr. Ford as the Bellman.)

"Just the place for a Snark!" the Bellman cried,
  "Just the place for a Snark, I declare!"
And he anchored the *Flivver* a mile up the river,
  And landed his crew with care.

He had bought a large map representing the moon,
  Which he spread with a runcible hand;
And the crew, you could see, were as pleased as could be
  With a map they could all understand.

"Now, listen, my friends, while I tell you again
  The five unmistakable marks
By which you may know, wherever you go,
  The warranted pacifist Snarks.

The first is the taste, which is something like guff,
  Tho' with gammon 'twill also compare;
The next is the sound, which is simple enough—
  It resembles escaping hot air.

The third is the shape, which is somewhat absurd,
  And this you will understand
When I tell you it looks like the African bird
  That buries its head in the sand.

The fourth is a want of the humorous sense,
  Of which it has hardly a hint.
And last, but not least, this marvelous beast
  Is a glutton for getting in print.

[168]

Now, Pacifist Snarks do no manner of harm,
  Yet I deem it my duty to say,
Some are Boojums——" The Bellman broke off in alarm,
  For Jane Addams had fainted away.

CONCERNING his reference to "Demosthenes' lantern," the distinguished culprit, Rupert Hughes, writes us that of course he meant Isosceles' lantern. The slip was pardonable, he urges, as he read proof on the line only seven times—in manuscript, in typescript, in proof for the magazine, in the copy for the book, in galley, in page-proof, and finally in the printed book. And heaven only knows how many proofreaders let it through. "Be that as it may," says Rupert, "I am like our famous humorist, Archibald Ward, who refused to be responsible for debts of his own contracting. And, anyway, I thank you for calling my attention to the blunder quietly and confidentially, instead of bawling me out in a public place where a lot of people might learn of it."

SORRY WE MISSED YOU.

Sir: . . . There were several things I wanted to say to you, and I proposed also to crack you over the sconce for what you have been saying about us Sinn Feiners. I suppose you're the sort that would laugh at this story:

He was Irish and badly wounded, unconscious

[169]

when they got him back to the dressing station, in a ruined village. "Bad case," said the docs. "When he comes out of his swoon he'll need cheering up. Say something heartening to him, boys. Tell him he's in Ireland." When the lad came to he looked around (ruined church on one side, busted houses, etc., up stage, and all that): "Where am I?" sez he. " 'S all right, Pat; you're in Ireland, boy." "Glory be to God!" sez he, looking around again. "How long have yez had Home Rule?"   TOM DALY.

OUR BOYS.

[From the Sheridan, Wyo., Enterprise.]

Our boys are off for the borders
Awaiting further orders
From our president to go
Down into old Mexico,
Where the Greaser, behind a cactus,
Is waiting to attack us.

THE skies they were ashen and sober, and the leaves they were crispèd and sere, as I sat in the porch chair and regarded our neighbor's patch of woodland; and I thought: The skies may be ashen and sober, and the leaves may be crispèd and sere, but in a maple wood we may dispense with the sun, such irradiation is there from the gold of the crispèd leaves. Jack Frost is as clever a wizard as the dwarf Rumpelstiltzkin, who

[170]

taught the miller's daughter the trick of spinning straw into gold. This young ash, robed all in yellow—what can the sun add to its splendor? And those farther tree-tops, that show against the sky like a tapestry, the slenderer branches and twigs, unstirred by wind, having the similitude of threads in a pattern—can the sun gild their refinèd gold? How delicate is the tinting of that cherry, the green of which is fading into yellow, each leaf between the two colors: this should be described in paint.

No, I said; in a hardwood thicket, in October, though it were the misty mid region of Weir, one would not know the sun was lost in clouds. At that moment the sun adventured forth, in blazing denial. It was as if the woodland had burst into flame.

As a variation of the story about the merchant who couldn't keep a certain article because so many people asked for it, we submit the following: A lady entered the rural drugstore which we patronize and said, "Mr. Blank, I want a bath spray." "I'm sorry, Mrs. Jones," sezze, "but the bath spray is sold."

IN A DEPARTMENT STORE.

Customer—"I want to look at some tunics."
Irish Floorwalker—"We don't carry musical instruments."

THAT Tennessee congressman who was arrested charged with operating an automobile while pifflicated, would reply that when he voted for prohibition he was representing his constituents, not his private thirst. Have we not, many times, in the good old days in Vermont, seen representatives rise with difficulty from their seats to cast their vote for prohibition? One can be pretty drunk and still be able to articulate "Ay."

A NEW drug, Dihydroxyphenylethylmethylamine, sounds as if all it needed was a raisin.

THE Gluck aria, which Mme. Homer has made famous, was effectively cited by the critic Hanslick to show that in vocal music the subject is determined only by the words. He wrote:
"At a time when thousands (among whom there were men like Jean Jacques Rousseau) were moved to tears by the air from 'Orpheus'—

> 'J'ai perdu mon Eurydice,
> Rien n'égale mon malheur,'

Boyé, a contemporary of Gluck, observed that precisely the same melody would accord equally well, if not better, with words conveying exactly the reverse, thus—

> 'J'ai trouvé mon Eurydice,
> Rien n'égale mon bonheur.'

"We, for our part, are not of the opinion that
[172]

in this case the composer is quite free from blame, inasmuch as music most assuredly possesses accents which more truly express a feeling of profound sorrow. If however, from among innumerable instances, we selected the one quoted, we have done so because, in the first place, it affects the composer who is credited with the greatest dramatic accuracy; and, secondly, because several generations hailed this very melody as most correctly rendering the supreme grief which the words express."

ARTHUR SHATTUCK sued for appreciation in Fond du Lac the other evening, playing, according to the Reporter, "a plaintiff melody with great tenderness." The jury returned a verdict in his favor without leaving their seats.

REPORTS of famine in China have recalled a remark about its excessive population. If the Chinese people were to file one by one past a given point the procession would never come to an end. Before the last man of those living to-day had gone by another generation would have grown up.

"SAY it with handkerchiefs," advertises a merchant in Goshen, Ind. That is, if the idea you wish to convey is that you have a cold in your head.

THE SOIL OF KANSAS.

[From the Kansas Farmer.]

Formed by the polyps of a shallow, summer sea; fixed by the subtile chemistry of the air, and comminuted by the Æolian geology of the Great Plains, the soil of Kansas has been one of man's richest possessions.

Why prose? The soil of Kansas, the Creator's masterpiece, invites to song. Frinstance—

> Formed by the polyps of a summer sea,
> Fixed by the subtile chemistry of air,
> Ground by Æolian geology,
> The soil of Kansas is beyond compare!

THE GOOD OLD DAYS.

Sir: An old stage hand at the Eau Claire opry house was talking. "No, sir, you don't see the actors to-day like we used to. Why, when Booth and Barrett played here you could hear them breathe way up in the fly gallery." E. C. M.

"WHAT THE LA HELLE!"

[From the Kankakee Republican.]

He helped tramp the old Hindenburg line, but this time, beating it on the strains of "Allons enfant de la Patrie le Jour de Gloire est de Triomphe et Arrivee!"

HERE is a characteristic bit of Vermontese that we picked up. A native was besought to saw some wood, but he declined. The owner of the wood offered double price for the sawing, and still the native declined. He was pressed for a reason, and this was it: "Damned if I'll humor a man."

"IT is not moral. It is immoral," declared an editorial colleague; and a reader is reminded of Lex Iconles, the old Greek baker of Grammer's Gap, Ark., who used to display in his window the enticing sign: "Doughnuts. Different and yet not the same."

THE mind of man is subject to many strange delusions, and one of these is that the stock market has a bottom.

THE manufacturer of a certain automobile advertises that his vehicle "will hold five ordinary people." And, as a matter of fact, it usually does.

THE Westminster Gazette headlines "The Intolerable Dullness of Country Life in Ireland." And Irene wonders what they would call excitement.

AN advertisement of dolls mentions, superfluously, that "some may not last the day." One does not expect them to.

THE London Mendicity Society estimates that £100,000 is given away haphazard every year to street beggars, and that the average beggar probably earns more than the average working man. There is talk of the beggars forming a union. A beggars' strike would be a fearsome thing.

> I WANT to be a diplomat
>   And with the envoys stand,
> A-wetting of my whistle in
>   A desiccated land.

The London Busman Story.

I.—As George Meredith might have related it.

"STOP!" she signalled.

The appeal was comprehensible, and the charioteer, assiduously obliging, fell to posture of checking none too volant steeds.

You are to suppose her past meridian, nearer the twilight of years, noteworthy rather for matter than manner; and her visage, comparable to the beef of England's glory, well you wot. This one's descent was mincing, hesitant, adumbrating dread of disclosures—these expectedly ample, columnar, massive. The day was gusty, the breeze prankant; petticoats, bandbox, umbrella were to be conciliated, managed if possible; no light task, you are to believe.

" 'Urry, marm!"

The busman's tone was patiently admonitory, dispassionate. A veteran in his calling, who had observed the ascending and descending of a myriad matrons, in playful gales.

" 'Urry, marm!"

The fellow was without illusions; he had reviewed more twinkling columns than a sergeant of drill. Indifference his note, leaning to ennui. He said so, bluntly, piquantly, in half a dozen memorable words, fetching yawn for period.

The lady jerked an indignant exclamation, and

[177]

completed, rosily precipitate, her passage to the pave.

II.—*As Henry James might have written it.*

We, let me ask, what are we, the choicer of spirits as well as the more frugal if not the undeservedly impoverished, what, I ask, are we to do now that the hansom has disappeared, as they say, from the London streets and the taxicab so wonderfully yet extravagantly taken its place? Is there, indeed, else left for us than the homely but hallowed 'bus, as we abbreviatedly yet all so affectionately term it—the 'bus of one's earlier days, when London was new to the unjaded sensorium and "Europe" was so wonderfully, so beautifully dawning on one's so avid and sensitive consciousness?

And fate, which has left us the 'bus—but oh, in what scant and shabby measure!—has left us, too, the weather that so densely yet so congruously "goes with it"—the weather adequately enough denoted by the thick atmosphere, the slimy pavements, the omnipresent unfurled umbrella and the stout, elderly woman intent upon gaining, at cost of whatever risk or struggle, her place and portion among the moist miscellany to whom the dear old 'bus—— But perhaps I have lost the thread of my sentence.

Ah, yes—that "stout, elderly woman"; so

superabundant whether as a type or as an individual; so prone—or "liable"—to impinge tyrannously upon the consciousness of her fellow-traveller, and in no less a degree upon that of the public servant, who, from his place aloft, guides, as it is phrased, the destinies of the conveyance. It was, indeed, one of the most notable of these—a humble friend of my own—who had the fortune to make the acute, recorded, historic observation which, with the hearty, pungent, cursory brevity and point of his class and *métier*—the envy of the painstaking, voluminous analyst and artist of our period—— But again I stray.

She was climbing up, or climbing down, perplexed equally, as I gather, by the management of her *parapluie* and of her—*enfin,* her petticoats. The candid anxiety of her round, underdone face, as she so wonderfully writhed to maintain the standard of pudicity dear—even vital—to the matron of the British Isles appealed—vividly, though mutely—to the forbearance that, seeing, would still seem *not* to see, her foot, her ankle, her *mollet*—as I early learned to say in Paris, where, however, so exigent a modesty is scarcely. . . . well, scarcely.

"Madam," the gracious fellow said in effect, *"ne vous gênez pas."* Then he went on to assure her briefly that he was an elderly man; that he had "held the ribbons," as they phrase it, for several years; that many were the rainy days in London; that each of these placed numerous women—elderly or younger—in the same involuntary predicament as that from which she herself had suffered; and that so far as he personally was concerned he had long since ceased to take any extreme delight in the—— *Bref,* he was charming; he renewed my fading belief—fading, as I had thought, disastrously but immitigably—in the capacity of the Anglo-Saxon for *esprit;* and I am glad indeed to have taken a line or so to record his *mot.*

III.—*As finally elucidated by Arnold Bennett.*

Maria Wickwyre, of the Five Towns, emerged from muddy Bombazine Lane and stood in the rain and wind at Pie Corner, eighty-four yards from the door of St. Jude's chapel, in the Strand. She was in London! Yes, she was on that spot, she and none other. It might have been somewhere else; it might have been somebody else. But it wasn't. Wonderful! The miracle of Life overcame her.

She had arms. Two of them. They were big and round, like herself. One held a large parcel ("package" for the American edition); the other, an umbrella. She also had two legs. She stood on them. If they had been absent, or if they had weakened, she would have collapsed. But they

[180]

held her up. Ah, the mysteries of existence! More than ever was she conscious of her firm, strong underpinning. Maria waved her umbrella and her parcel and stopped a 'bus. The driver was elderly, wrinkled, weatherbeaten. Maria got in and rode six furlongs and some yards to Mooge Road, and then she stopped the 'bus to get out.

If she was conscious of her upper members and their charges, she was still more conscious of her lower ones. If she had her parcel and her umbrella to think about, she also had her stockings and petticoats to consider. The wind blew, the rain drizzled, the driver looked around, wondering why Maria didn't get out and have done with it.

"If he should see them!" she gasped. (You know what she meant by "them.") Her round, broad face mutely implored the 'busman to look the other way.

He wearily closed his eyes. He had been rumbling through the Strand for thirty years. "Lor', mum," he said, "legs ain't no treat to me!"

Maria collapsed, after all, and took the 4:29 for home that same afternoon.

A LINE-O'-TYPE OR TWO

Hew to the Line, let the
quips fall where they may.

APRILLY.

WHAN that Aprillè with hise shourès soote
　　The droghte of March had percèd to the roote,
I druv a motor thro' Aprillè's bliz
Somme forty mile, and dam neere lyke to friz.

HARRIET reports the first trustworthy sign of spring: friend husband on the back porch Sunday morning removing last year's mud from his golf shoes.

OLD DOC Oldfield of London prescribes dandelion leaves, eggs, lettuce, milk, and a few other things for people who would live long, and a Massachusetts centenarian offers, as her formula, "Don't worry and don't over-eat." But we, whose mission is to enlighten the world, rather than to ornament it, are more influenced by the experiment of Herbert Spencer. Persuaded to a vegetarian diet, he stuck at it for six months. Then reading over what he had written during that time, he thrust the manuscript into the fire and ordered a large steak with fried potatoes and mushrooms.

[183]

"SPRING HAS COME . . ."

The trees were rocked by April's blast;
  A frozen robin fell,
And twittered, as he breathed his last,
  "Lykelle, lykelle, lykelle."

BYRON WROTE MOST OF THIS.
[From the Monticello Times.]

Julf Husman, who has been busy for the past several months, building a fine new house and barn, celebrated their completion with a barn dance Wednesday night. "The beauty and chivalry" of Wayne and adjoining townships attended, and did "chase the glowing hours with flying feet," with as much enthusiasm and pleasure as did the guests "When Belgium's capital had gathered then and bright the lamps shone over fair women and brave men."

A CANNERY DANCE.
[From the Iowa City Press.]

"Fair women and brave men" circled hither and thither in the maze of the stately waltz and the festal two-step, and the dainty slippers kept graceful time with the strains of the exceptionally fine music of the hour. Lovely young women, with roses in their cheeks and their hair, caught the reflection of the radiant electric lights and the

[184]

glory of the superb decorations, and their natural pulchritude was enhanced in impressiveness thereby. The "frou frou" of silks and satins; the enchanting orchestral offerings; the brilliant illuminations; the alluring decorations, and the intoxication of the dance made the event one of the most markedly successful in the history of the university.

FOR THE LAST DAY OF MARCH.

> Just before you go to bed,
> Push the clock an hour ahead.
>
> Little Mary.

Don't forget to set the time locks on your safes ahead an hour. Otherwise you'll be all mixed up.

At Ye Olde Colonial Inn, according to the Aurora Beacon-News, a special "Table de Haute" dinner was served last Sunday. And the Gem restaurant in St. Louis tells the world: "Our famous steaks tripled our seating capacity."

CHANCES, 2; ERRORS, 2.

Sir: While in the Hotel Dyckman I noted a sign recommending the 85c dinner in the "Elizabethian Room." After a search I found the place, duly labeled "Elizabethean Room."

D. K. M.

Just what does the trade jargon mean, "Experience essential but not necessary"? We see it frequently in the advertising columns.

A variant of the form, "experience essential but not necessary," is used by the Racine Times-Call, as follows:

"Wanted, secretary-treasurer for a local music corporation; must also have a knowledge of music, but not essential."

As curious as the advertising form, "experience essential but not necessary," is the form used by the Daily News: "Responsible for no debts contracted by no other than myself."

The provincialism indicated by the title of the pop song, "Good bye, Broadway! Hello, France!" reminds us of the headline in a New York paper some years ago: "Halley's Comet Rushing on New York."

"The love, the worship of truth is the most essential thing in journalism," says the editor of Le Matin. Or, as the ads read, "love of truth essential but not necessary."

The Hopkinsville, Ky., News is a Negro paper, and its motto is: "Man is made of clay, and like a meerschaum pipe is more valuable when highly colored."

FROM the letter of a colored gentleman of leisure, apropos of his wife's suit for divorce: "P. S.: Also, honey, i hope while others have your company i may have your heart." Here is a refrain for a sentimental song.

SMACK! SMACK!

Sir: May I suggest that the matrimonial bureau of the Academy take steps to introduce Miss Irene V. Smackem of Washington, D.C., and Mr. Kissinger of Fergus Falls, Minn.? They would make a perfect pair.   KAYE.

MARCH.

With heart of gold and yellow frill,
Arcturus, like a daffodil,
Now dances in the field of gray
Upon the East at close of day;
A joyous harbinger to bring
The many promises of spring!

W.

IF no one else cares, the compositor and proof reader will be interested to know that Ignacy Seczupakiewicz brought suit in Racine against Praxida Seczupakiewicz.

REFERRING to Beethoven's anniversary, Ernest Newman remarks that "a truly civilized community would probably celebrate a centenary by prohibiting all performances of the master's works for three or five years, so that the public's deadening familiarity with them might wear off. That would be the greatest service it could do him."

NEWMAN, by the way, is a piano-player fan, contending that when the principles of beautiful tone production are understood, mechanical means will probably come nearer to perfection than the human hand. Mr. Arthur Whiting, considering the horseless pianoforte some time ago, was also enthusiastic. The h. p. is entirely self-possessed, and has even more platform imperturbability than the applauded virtuoso. "After a few introductory sounds, which have nothing to do with the music, and without relaxing the lines of its inscrutable face, the insensate artist proceeds to show its power. Its security puts all hand playing to shame; it never hesitates, it surmounts the highest difficulties without changing a clutch."

DIXON's Elks were entertained t'other evening by the Artists Trio, and the Telegraph observes that "one of the remarkable facts concerning this company is that while they are finished artists they nevertheless are delightful entertainers."

WE seldom listen to a canned-music machine, but when we do we realize the great educational value of the discs. They advise us (especially the records of singing comedians) what to avoid.

THE prejudices against German music will deprive many gluttons for punishment of the opportunity to hear "Parsifal." We remember one lady who was concerned because Dalmorés stood for a long time with his back to the audience. "Why does he have to do that?" she asked her companion. "Because," was the answer, "he shot the Holy Grail."

AT a concert in Elmira, N. Y., according to the Telegram, William Kincade sang "Tolstoi's Good Bye." Some one sings it every now and then.

AMONG the forty-six professors removed from the universities of Greece were, we understand, all those holding the chair of Greek. Another blow at the classics.

LITERATURE.

A great deal of very good writing has been done by invalids, but it is not likely that anybody

[189]

ever produced a line worth remembering while suffering with a plain cold.

WE were saying to our friend Dr. Empedocles that we kept our enthusiasms green by never taking anything very seriously. "That's interesting," said he: "I, too, have kept my enthusiasm fresh, and I have always taken everything seriously." The two notions seemed irreconcilable, but we presently agreed that by having a great number and variety of enthusiasms one is not likely to ride any of them to death. We all know persons who wear out an enthusiasm by taking it as solemnly as they would a religious rite.

WE were sure that the headline, "Mint at Chicago Greatly Needed, Houston Says," would inspire more than one reader to remark that the mint is the least important part of the combination.

WE are reminded of the experience of a friend who has a summer place in Connecticut. At church the pastor announced a fund for some war charity, and asked for contributions. Our friend sent in fifty dollars, and a few days later inquired of the pastor how much money had been raised, "Fifty-five dollars and seventy-five cents," was the answer. The pastor had contributed five dollars.

SONG.

[In the manner of Laura Blackburn.]

I quested Love with timid feet,
  And many qualms and perturbations—
Hoping yet fearing we should meet,
  Because I knew my limitations.

When Love I spied I fetched a sigh—
  A sigh a Tristan might expire on:
"I must apologize," said I,
  "For not resembling Georgie Byron."

Love laughed and said, "You know I'm blind,"
  And pinched my ear, the little cutie!
"Her heart and yours shall be entwined,
  Tho' you were twice as shy on beauty."

THROWING self-interest to the winds, a Chicago sweetshop advertises: "That we may have a part in the effort to bring back normal conditions and reduce the high cost of living, our prices on chocolates and bon-bons are now one dollar and fifty cents per pound."

PERSONS who are so o. f. as to like rhyme with their poetry may discover another reason for their preference in the following passage, which Edith Wyatt quotes from Oscar Wilde:

"Rime, that exquisite echo which in the Muse's hollow hill creates and answers its own voice; rime, which in the hands of the real artist becomes not merely a material element of material beauty, but a spiritual element of thought and passion also, waking a new mood, it may be, or stirring a fresh train of ideas, or opening by mere sweetness and suggestion of sound some golden door at which the Imagination itself had knocked in vain; rime which can turn man's utterance to the speech of gods"—

WE promised Miss Wyatt that the next time we happened on the parody of Housman's "Lad," we would reprint it; and yesterday we stumbled on it. Voila!—

THE BELLS OF FROGNAL LANE.

They sound for early Service
  The bells of Frognal Lane;
And I am thinking of the day
  I shot my cousin Jane.

At Frognal Lane the Service
  Begins at half-past eight,
And some folk get there early
  While others turn up late.

But, come they late or early,
   I ne'er shall be again
The careless chap of days gone by
   Before I murdered Jane.

WE have been looking over "Forms Suggested for Telegraph Messages," issued by the Western Union. While more humorous than perhaps was intended, they fall short of the forms suggested by Max Beerbohm, in "How Shall I Word It?" As for example:

LETTER IN ACKNOWLEDGEMENT OF WEDDING PRESENT.

Dear Lady Amblesham,
Who gives quickly, says the old proverb, gives twice. For this reason I have purposely delayed writing to you, lest I should appear to thank you more than once for the small, cheap, hideous present you sent me on the occasion of my recent wedding. Were you a poor woman, that little bowl of ill-imitated Dresden china would convict you of tastelessness merely; were you a blind woman, of nothing but an odious parsimony. As you have normal eyesight and more than normal wealth, your gift to me proclaims you at once a Philistine and a miser (or rather did so proclaim you until, less than ten seconds after I had unpacked it from its wrappings of tissue paper, I

[193]

took it to the open window and had the satisfaction of seeing it shattered to atoms on the pavement). But stay! I perceive a flaw in my argument. Perhaps you were guided in your choice by a definite wish to insult me. I am sure, on reflection, that this is so. *I shall not forget.*

Yours, etc.

CYNTHIA BEAUMARSH.

PS. My husband asks me to tell you to warn Lord Amblesham to keep out of his way or to assume some disguise so complete that he will not be recognized by him and horsewhipped.

PPS. I am sending copies of this letter to the principal London and provincial newspapers.

WE hope that Max Beerbohm read far enough in Bergson to appreciate what Mr. Santayana says of that philosopher. He seems to feel, wrote G. S. (we quote from memory), that all systems of philosophy existed in order to pour into him, which is hardly true, and that all future systems would flow out of him, which is hardly necessary.

To a great number of people all reasoning and comment is superficial that is not expressed in the jargon of sociology and political economy. Expand a three-line paragraph in that manner and it becomes profound.

SING A SONG OF SPRINGTIME.

Sing a song of springtime, things begin to grow;
Four and twenty bluebirds darting to and fro;
When the morning opened the birds began to sing.
Wasn't that a pretty day to set before a king!

The King was on the golf links, chopping up the ground;
The Queen was in the garden, planting seeds around.
When the King returned, after many wasted hours,
"Don't ever say," the Queen exclaimed, "that you are
      fond of flowers."

MIKE NECKYOKE drives a taxi in Rhinelander,
Wis., and you have only one guess at what he used
to drive.

FROM Philadelphia comes word of the nuptials
of Mr. Tunis and Miss Fisch. Tunis, we leap-
ingly conclude, is the masculine form!

WE have the card of another chimney sweep,
who is "sole agent for wind in chimneys and fur-
naces." His name is MacDraft, which may be
another nom de flume.

THE anti-fat brigade may be intrigued to learn
that Mr. George Squibb of Wareham, Eng.,
sought death in the sea at Swanage, but was unable to stay under the water because of his
corpulence.

NOT long ago a mule broke a leg by kicking a man in the head, and this week a horse broke a leg in the same way; in each case the man was not seriously injured. Is this merely luck, or is evolution modifying the human coco?

MORE building is the solution of the unemployment problem. The unemployed are never so occupied and contented as when watching the construction of a sky-scraper.

HER publishers having announced that Ellen Glasgow has "gone into leather," Keith Preston explains that going into leather is "like receiving the accolade, taking the veil, or joining the American Academy of Arts and Letters." And we suppose that when one goes into ooze leather, or is padded, one may be said to be fini.

A FEW MORE "BEST BAD LINES."

Why leapest thou,
Why leapest thou
    So high within my breast?
Oh, stay thee now,
Oh, stay thee now,
    Thou little bounder, rest!
                    —Ruskin (at 12).

Something had happened wrong about a bill,
Which was not drawn with true mercantile skill,

So to amend it I was told to go
To seek the firm of Clutterbuck & Co.

      —George Crabbe.

But let me not entirely overlook
The pleasure gathered from the rudiments
Of geometric science.

      —Wordsworth.

Israel in ancient days
Not only had a view
Of Sinai in a blaze,
But heard the Gospel too.

      —Cowper.

Flashed from his bed the electric message came;
He is no better; he is much the same.

     —A Cambridge prize poem.

A HOUSEHOLD hinter advises that "if the thin white curtains blow into the gas and catch fire sew small lead weights into the seams." Before doing this, however, it would be wise to turn in an alarm.

THE orchestra was playing too loud to suit the manager, so he complained to the leader. "The passage is written in forte," said the latter. "Well, make it about thirty-five."

SEIZE HIM, SCOUTS!

Sir: I submit for the consideration of the new school of journalism the following, recently perpetrated by an aspiring young journalist: "Information has been received that Mrs. Blank,

[197]

who was spending a vacation of several weeks in Colorado, was killed in an automobile accident over long distance telephone by her husband."

CALCITROSUS.

"THAT'S GOOD."

Sir: A man and three girls were waiting for the bus. The driver slowed up long enough to call, "Full house!" "Three queens!" responded the waiting cit, and turned disgustedly away.

X. T. C.

WHY BANK CLERKS ARE TIRED.

Sir: Voice over the telephone: "Please send me two check books."

B. C.: "Large or small?"

V. o. t. t.: "Well, I don't write such very large checks, but sometimes they amount to a hundred dollars."

JANE.

"WHY not make room for daddy?" queries the editor of the Emporia Gazette, with a break in his voice. Daddy, we hardly need say, is the silently suffering member of the household who hasn't a large closet all to himself, with rows of shiny hooks on which to hang his duds.

Ah, yes, why not make room for daddy? It is impossible to contemplate daddy's pathetic condition without bursting into tears. Votes for women? Huh! Hooks for men!

"NATION-WIDE."

How anybody can abide
That punk expression, "nation-wide"—

How one can view unhorrified
That vile locution, nation-wide,

I cannot see. I almost died
When first I spotted nation-wide.

On every hand, on every side,
On every page, is nation-wide.

To everything it is applied;
No matter what, it's nation-wide.

The daily paper's pet and pride:
They simply dote on nation-wide.

It seem's if each with t'other vied
To make the most of nation-wide.

No doubt the proof-room Argus-eyed
Approves the "style" of nation-wide.

My colleagues fall for it, but I'd
Be damned if I'd use nation-wide.

It gets my goat, and more beside,
That phrase atrocious, nation-wide.

Abomination double-dyed,
Away, outrageous "nation-wide"!

SPEAKING of local color, B. Humphries Brown and Bonnie Blue were wedded in Indianapolis.

MARRIED, in Evansville, Ind., Ellis Shears and Golden Lamb.   Something might be added about wool-gathering.

EMBARRASSED by the riches of modern literature at our elbow, we took refuge in Jane Austen, and re-read "Mansfield Park," marvelling again at its freshness.   They who hold that Mark Twain was not a humorist, or that he was at best an incomplete humorist, have an argument in his lack of appreciation of Jane Austen.

ONE of the most delightful things about the author of "Mansfield Park" that we have seen lately is an extract from "Personal Aspects of Jane Austen," by Miss Austen-Leigh.   "Each of the novels," she says, "gives a description, closely interwoven with the story and concerned with its principal characters, of error committed, conviction following, and improvement effected, all of which may be summed up in the word 'Repentance.' "

ALMOST as good is Miss Austen-Leigh's contradiction of the statement that sermons wearied Jane.   She quotes the author's own words: "I am very fond of Sherlock's Sermons, and prefer them to almost any." What a lot of amusement she must have had, shooting relatives and friends through the hat!

Was there ever a character more delightfully detestable than Mrs. Norris? Was there ever another character presented, so alive and breathing, in so few pen strokes? Jane Austen had no need of psychoanalysis.

As for William Lyons Phelps' remark, which a contrib has quoted, that "too much modern fiction is concerned with unpleasant characters whom one would not care to have as friends," how would you like to spend a week-end with the characters in "The Mayor of Casterbridge"? With the exception of the lady in "Two on a Tower," and one or two others, Mr. Hardy's characters are not the sort that one would care to be cast away with; yet will we sit the night out, book in hand, to follow their sordid fortunes.

"What I want to know is," writes Fritillaria, "whether you think Jane Austen drew Edmund and Fanny for models, or knew them for the unconscionable prigs they are. I am collecting votes." Well, we think that Jane knew they were prigs, but nevertheless had, like ourself, a

warm affection for Fanny. Fanny Price, Elizabeth Bennet, and Anne (we forget her last name)
are three of the dearest girls in fiction.

WE are reminded by F. B. T. that the last name
of the heroine of "Persuasion" was Elliott.
Anne is our favorite heroine—except when we
think of Clara Middleton.

SPACE has been reserved for us in the archæo-
logical department of the Field Museum for Pre-
Dry wheezes, which should be preserved for a
curious posterity. We have filed No. 1, which
runs:
"First Comedian: 'Well, what made you get
drunk in the first place?' Second Comedian: 'I
didn't get drunk in the first place. I got drunk in
the last place.' "

OUR budding colyumist (who, by the way, has
not thanked us for our efforts in his behalf) will
want that popular restaurant gag: "Use one
lump of sugar and stir like hell. We don't mind
the noise."

"WHAT," queries R. W. C., "has become of the
little yellow crabs that floated in the o. f. oyster
stew?" Junsaypa. We never found out what
became of the little gold safety pins that used to
come with neckties.

AN innovation at the Murdock House in Shawano, Wis., is "Bouillon in cups," instead of the conventional tin dipper.

BY the way, has any candid merchant ever advertised a Good Riddance Sale?

MUCH has been written about Mr. Balfour in the last twelvemonth; and Mr. Balfour himself has published a book, a copy of which we are awaiting with more or less impatience. Mr. Balfour is not considered a success as a statesman, because he has always looked upon politics merely as a game; and Frank Harris once wrote that if A. B. had had to work for a living he might have risen to original thought—whatever that may imply.

WHAT we have always marveled at is Balfour's capacity for mental detachment. In the first year of the war he found time to deliver, extempore, the Gifford lectures, and in the next year he published "Theism and Humanism." It is said, of course, that he had a great gift for getting or allowing other people to do his work in the war council and the admiralty; but that does not entirely explain his brimming mind.

"THERE is a fine old man," as one of our readers reported his Irish gardener as saying of A. B.

"Did you know Mr. Balfour?" he was asked. "Did I know him?" was the reply. "Didn't I help rotten-egg him in Manchester twenty-five years ago!"

Col. Fanny Butcher relates that the average reader who patronizes the New York public library prefers Conan Doyle's detective stories to any others. Quite naturally. There is more artistry in Poe, and the tales about the Frenchman, Arsène Lupin, are ten times more ingenious than Doyle's; but Doyle has infused the adventures of Sherlock Holmes with the undefinable something known as romance, and that has preserved them. The great majority of detective stories are merely ingenious.

Col. Butcher says she uses "The Crock of Gold" to test the minds of people. A friend of ours employs "Zuleika Dobson" for the same purpose. What literary acid do *you* apply?

Our compliments to Mrs. Borah, who possesses a needed sense of humor. "If," she is reported as saying to her husband, "if it were not for the pleasures of life you might enjoy it."

A librarian confides to us that she was visited by a young lady who wished to see a *large* map of France. She was writing a paper on the battlefields of France for a culture club, and she just couldn't find Flanders' Fields and No Man's Land on any of the maps in her books.

A SIGN, reported by B. R. J., in a Cedar Rapids bank announces: "We loan money on Liberty bonds. No other security required." Showing that here and there you will find a banker who is willing to take a chance.

THE first object of the National Parks association is "to fearlessly defend the national parks and monuments against assaults of private interests." May we not hope that the w. k. infinitive also may be preserved intact?

A MISSIONARY from the Chicago Woman's Club lectured in Ottawa on better English and less slang, and the local paper headed its story: "Bum Jabber Binged on Beezer by Jane With Trick Lingo."

YOUNG GRIMES tells us that he would like to share in the advantages of Better Speech weeks, but does not know where to begin. We have started him off with the word "February." If at the end of the week he can pronounce it Feb-ru-ary we shall give him the word "address."

"THIS, being Better English week, everyone is doing their best to improve their English."—Quincy, Mich., Herald.

Still, Jane Austen did it.

BETTER ENGLISH IN THE BEANERY.

Waiter: "Small on two—well!"
Chef: "Small well on two!"   TIP.

HAPPY THOUGHT.

This world is so full of a number of singers,
We need not be bluffed any longer by ringers.

The Magic Kit.

A FAIRY TALE FOR SYMPATHETIC ELDERS.

I.

ONCE upon a time, not far removed from yesterday, there lived a poor book reviewer named Abner Skipp. He was a kindly man and an excellent husband and a most congenial soul to chat with, for he possessed a store of information on the most remote and bootless subjects drawn from his remarkable library—an accumulation of volumes sent to him for review, and which he had been unable to dispose of to the dealers in second-hand books. For you are to understand that too little literary criticism is done on a cash basis. Occasionally a famous author, like Mr. Howells, is paid real money to write something about Mr. James, or Mr. James is substantially rewarded for writing about Mr. Howells, and heads of departments and special workers are handsomely remunerated; but the journeyman reviewer is paid in books; and these are the source of his income.

Thus, every morning in the busy season, or perhaps once a week when trade was dull, Abner Skipp journeyed from the suburbs to the city with his pack of books on his back, and made the rounds of the second-hand shops, disposing of his wares for whatever they would fetch. Novels, especially what are known as the "best sellers," commanded good prices if they were handled, like fruit, without delay; but they were such perishable merchandise that oftentimes a best seller was dead before Abner could get it to market; and as he frequently reviewed the same novel for half a dozen employers, and therefore had half a dozen copies of it in his pack, the poor wretch was sadly out of pocket, being compelled to sell the dead ones to the junkman for a few pennies.

Abner Skipp was an industrious artisan and very skillful at his trade; working at top speed, he could review more than a hundred books in a day of eight hours. In a contest of literary critics held in Madison Square Garden, New York, Abner won first prize in all three events—reviewing by publisher's slip, reviewing by cover, and reviewing by title page. But shortly after this achievement he had had the misfortune to sprain his right arm in reviewing a new edition of the Encyclopedia Britannica, which accident so curtailed his earning power that he fell behind in a money way, and was compelled to mortgage his home. But Abner Skipp was a cheerful, buoyant soul; and as his arm grew better and he was again able to wield the implements of his trade, he set bravely to work to mend his broken fortunes.

II.

If Abner Skipp had had nothing but popular
novels to review he would assuredly have perished
of starvation, but frequently he received a medical work, or a history, or a volume of sportive
philosophy by William James, or some such
valuable work, which he could sell for a round
sum. There was always plenty to do—all the
best magazines employed him, and twice in the
year—a month in spring and a month in fall—
books came to him in such numbers that the expressman dumped them into the house through
a shute like so many coals.

Mrs. Skipp assisted her husband all she could,
but being a frail little woman she was able to
work on only the lightest fiction. Angelica, the
oldest daughter, cleared the book bin of a good
deal of poetry and gift books, and even Grandpa
Skipp was intrusted with a few juveniles.

But none of the family was more helpful than
little Harold, who, after school time, worked side
by side with his father, trimming the ready made
review slips which publishers send out with books,
and seeing that the paste pot never got empty or
the paste too thick. Harold, as his father often
proudly observed, was a born book reviewer.
From infancy it was observed that the outside
of a book always interested him more than the inside, and once when his school teacher directed

him to write a sentence containing the word "book," he wrote: "The book is attractively bound and is profusely illustrated."

One evening, in the very busiest week of the busy season, little Harold's was the only bright face at the supper table. Abner Skipp had had a bad day in the city; Mrs. Skipp and Angelica were exhausted from reviewing and household cares, and Grandpa was peevish because Abner had taken the "Pea Green Fairy Book" away from him and given him instead a "Child's History of the Congo Free State."

"What is the matter, Abner?" his wife asked him when the others of the family had retired. "Does your arm hurt you again?"

"No, wife," replied Abner Skipp. "My arm does not trouble me; I have handled only the lightest literature for the last fortnight. Alas! it is the same old worry. The interest on the mortgage will be due again next week, and in spite of the fact that the cellar is so full of books that I can scarcely get into it, we have not a dollar above the sum required to meet our monthly bills."

III.

"Alas!" exclaimed the hapless Abner Skipp, next morning, "it seems as if nothing was being published this fall except popular novels, and I obtained an average of less than twenty cents on the last sackload I took to town, not counting the dead ones which I sold to the junkman."

"If only there were some way of keeping them alive for a few days longer!" said Mrs. Skipp. "If one could only stimulate the heart action by injecting strychnine!"

"Or even embalm them," said Abner, sharing his wife's grewsome humor. "But no; it is impossible to deceive a second-hand bookseller. He seems to know to the minute when a novel is dead, and declines to turn his shop into a literary morgue." The poor man sighed. "If my employers would send me a few volumes of biography, or an encyclopedia, or a set of Shakespeare, we could easily meet the interest on the mortgage."

"I wish, Abner, that I could be of more help to you," said Mrs. Skipp. "If I could break myself of the habit of glancing at the last chapter of a novel before reviewing it, I could do ever so many more. Angelica is even more thoughtless than I. The poor child declares that some of the stories look so interesting that she forgets her work completely and actually begins to read them. As for Grandpa, he always was a great reader, and consequently has no head at all for reviewing."

"If Harold were a few years older——" mused Abner. "But there, wife, we must not spend in

vain repining the scant hours allotted to us for
sleep. Perhaps the expressman will bring us some
scientific books to-morrow. Quite a number were
on Appletree's fall list."

Abner Skipp kissed his wife affectionately, and
presently the house was dark and still. Mrs.
Skipp, worn out by the day's work, went quickly
to sleep; but Abner, haunted by the mortgage,
passed a restless night. Several times he fancied
he heard a noise in the cellar, as if the expressman
were dumping another ton of books into the bin.
At last, just before dawn, there came a loud
thump, as if a volume of Herbert Spencer's Autobiography had fallen to the floor. Getting out
of bed quietly so that his weary wife should not
be disturbed, Abner went to the cellar stairway
and listened.

A clicking sound was distinctly audible, and a
faint light gleamed below.

IV.

Cautiously descending the stair, Abner Skipp
came upon so strange a sight that with difficulty
he restrained himself from crying out his aston-
ishment. Little Harold was seated before a
queer mechanism, which resembled a typewriter,
spinning wheel, and adding machine combined,
engaged in turning the tons of books around him
into reviews, as the miller's daughter spun the

straw into gold, in the ancient tale of "Rumpel-stiltzkin."

"Child, what does this mean?" cried the bewildered Abner Skipp. "Father," replied Harold, "I am lifting the mortgage. Not long ago I saw among the advertisements in the Saturday Home Herald an announcement of a Magic Kit for book reviewers, with a capacity of 300 books per hour. Fortunately I had enough money in my child's bank to pay the first installment on this wonderful outfit which came to-day. Is it not a marvelous invention, father? Even Grandpa could work it!" Trembling with eagerness Abner Skipp bent over the Magic Kit, while little Harold explained the working of the various parts.

To review a book all that was necessary was to press a few keys, pull a lever or two, and the thing was done. Reviewing by publisher's slip was simplicity itself; the slips were dropped into a hopper, and presently emerged neatly gummed to sheets of copy paper; and if an extract from the book were desired, a page was quickly torn out and fed in with the slip. Reviewing by title page was almost as rapid. The operator typewrote the title, author's name, publisher, price, and number of pages, and then pulled certain levers controlling the necessary words and phrases, such as—

[213]

"This latest work is not likely to add to the author's reputation"; or—

"The book will appeal chiefly to specialists"; or—

"An excellent tale to while away an idle hour"; or—

"The book is attractively bound and is profusely illustrated."

"Father," said little Harold, his face glowing, "to-morrow we will hire a furniture van and take all these books to the city."

"My boy," cried Abner Skipp, folding his little son in his arms, "you are the little fairy in our home. Surely no other could have done this job more neatly or with greater dispatch; and no fairy wand could be more wonder-working than this truly Magic Kit."

A LINE-O'-TYPE OR TWO

"Fay ce que vouldras."

TO B. L. T.
(Quintus Horatius Flaccus loquitur.)

Maecenas sprang from royal line,
  You spring a Line diurnal.
(Perhaps my joke is drawn too fine
  For readers of your journal.)

But what I started out to say,
  Across the gulf of ages,
Is that, in our old Roman day,
  My patron paid me wages.

No barren wreath of fame was mine
  When Mac approved my stuff,
But casks of good Falernian wine,
  And slaves and gold enough.

And last, to keep the wolf away
  And guard my age from harm,
He gave me in his princely way
  My little Sabine farm.

But now, forsooth, your merry crew—
  O Tempora! O Mores!—
What do they ever get from you—
  Your Laura, Pan, Dolores?

[215]

They fill the Line with verse and wheeze,
  To them your fame is due.
What do they ever get for these?
  Maecenas? Ha! Ha! *You?*

So as I quaff my spectral wine.
  At ease beside the Styx,
Would I contribute to the Line?
  Nequaquam! Nunquam! Nix!

CAMPION.

OUR compliments to Old Man Flaccus, whose witty message reminds us to entreat contribs to be patient, as we are snowed under with offerings. For a week or more we have been trying to horn into the column with some verses of our own composing.

BRIGHT SAYINGS OF MOTHER.

My respected father came to breakfast on New Year's Day remarking that he had treated himself to a present by donning a new pair of suspenders, whereupon mother remarked: "Well braced for the New Year, as it were!"   C. T. S.

AFTER some years of editing stories of events in high society, a gentleman at an adjacent desk believes he has learned the chief duty of a butler. It is to call the police.

"THAT STRAIN AGAIN—IT HAD A DYING SNORT."

Sir: Speaking of soft music and the pearly gates, S. T. Snortum is owner and demonstrator of the music store at St. Peter, Minnesota.

S. W. E.

WARREN, O., has acquired a lady barber, and dinged if her name isn't Ethel Gillette.

No doubt the Manistee News-Advocate has its reason for running the "hogs received" news under the heading "Hotel Arrivals."

"I SEE by an announcement by the Columbia Mills that window shades are down," communicates W. H. B. "Can it be that the Columbia Mills people are ashamed of something?" Mebbe. Or perhaps they are fixing prices.

"FOR the lovamike," requests the Head Scene-Shifter, "keep the Admirable Crichton out of the Column. We have twenty-five presses, and it takes a guard at each press to prevent it from appearing Admiral Crichton."

PITTSBURGH Shriners gave a minstrel show the other night, and the inspired reporter for the Post mentions that "an intermission separated the two parts and broke the monotony."

A BACH chaconne is on the orchestra programme this week. Some one remarked that he did not care for chaconnes, which moved us to quote what some one else (we think it was Herman Devries) said: "Chaconne à son goût."

"POND AND POND Donate $500 to Union Pool Fund."—Ann Arbor item.
Quite so.

IF we had not been glancing through the real estate notes we should never have known that Mystical Schriek lives in Evansville, Ind.

FROM the Illinois Federal Reporter: "Village of Westville vs. Albert Rainwater. Mr. Rainwater is charged with violation of the ordinance in regard to the sale of soft drinks." Can Al have added a little hard water to the mixture?

MEMORY TESTS FOR THE HOME.

Sir: Friend wife was naming authors of various well known novels, as I propounded their titles. Follows the result:
Me: "The Last Days of Pompeii." She: "Dante."
"Les Miserables." "Huguenot."
"Adam Bede." "Henry George."

[218]

"Vanity Fair." "Why, that's in Ecclesiastes."
"Ben Hur." "Rider Haggard."
"The Pilgrim's Progress." "John Barley-corn."
"Don Quixote." (No reply.)
"Waverly." "Oh, did Waverly write that?"
"Anna Karenina." "Count Leon Trotsky."

J. C.

WE see by the Fargo papers that Mrs. Bernt
Wick gave a dinner recently, and we hope that
Miss Candle, the w. k. night nurse, was among
the guests.

LEVI BEIN' A GOOD SPORT.

Sir: Levi Frost, the leading druggist of Milton
Falls, Vt., set a big bottle of medicine in his show
window with a sign sayin' he'd give a phonograph to anybody who could tell how many
spoonfuls there was in the bottle. Jed Ballard
was comin' downstreet, and when he seen the sign
he went and he sez, sezzee, "Levi," sezzee, "if
you had a spoon big enough to hold it all, you'd
have just one spoonful in that bottle." And, by
Judas Priest, Levi give him the phonograph right
off. HIRAM.

"BASING his sermon on the words of Gesta Romanorum, who in 1473 said, 'What I spent I had,

[219]

what I kept I lost, what I gave I have,' the Rev. Albert H. Zimmerman," etc.—Washington Post.

As students of the School of Journalism ought to know, the philosopher Gesta Romanorum was born in Sunny, Italy, although some historians claim Merry, England, and took his doctor's degree at the University of Vivela, in Labelle, France. His Latin scholarship was nothing to brag of, but he was an ingenious writer. He is best known, perhaps, as the author of the saying, "Rome was not built in a day," and the line which graced the flyleaf of his first edition, "Viae omniae in Romam adducunt."

"IT is a great misfortune," says Lloyd George, "that the Irish and the English are never in the same temper at the same time." Nor is that conjuncture encouragingly probable. But there is hope. Energy is required for strenuous rebellion, and energy is converted into heat and dissipated. If, or as, the solar system is running down, its stock of energy is constantly diminishing; and so the Irish Question will eventually settle itself, as will every other mess on this slightly flattened sphere.

WHENEVER you read about England crumbling, turn to its automobile Blue Book and observe this: "It must be remembered that in all countries except England and New Zealand automobiles travel on the wrong side of the road."

THE first sign of "crumbling" on the part of the British empire that we have observed is the welcome extended to the "quick lunch." That may get 'em.

LOST AND FOUND.

[Song in the manner of Laura Blackburn.]

Whilst I mused in vacant mood
  By a wild-thyme banklet,
Love passed glimmering thro' the wood,
  Lost her golden anklet.

Followed I as fleet as dart
  With the golden token;
But she vanished—and my heart,
  Like the clasp, is broken.

Such a little hoop of gold!
  She . . . but how compare her?
Till Orion's belt grow cold
  I shall quest the wearer.

Next my heart I've worn it since,
  More than life I prize it,
And, like Cinderella's prince,
  I must advertise it.

WOULD you mind contributing a small sum, say a dollar or two, to the Keats Memorial Fund. We thought not. It is a privilege and a pleasure. The object is to save the house in which the poet lived during his last years, and in which he did some of his best work. The names of all contributors will be preserved in the memorial house, so it would be a nice idea to send your dollar or two in the name of your small child or grandchild, who may visit Hampstead when he grows up. Still standing in the garden at Hampstead is the plum tree under which Keats wrote,

"Thou wast not born for death, immortal Bird!
No hungry generations tread thee down."

AMERICANS who speak at French should confine their conversation to other Americans similarly talented. They should not practise on French people, whose delicate ear is no more proof against impure accent than a stone is proof against dripping water. The mistake which English speaking people make is assuming that French is merely a language, whereas, even in Paris, the speaking of it as much as accomplishment as singing, or painting on china. Many gifted Frenchmen, like M. Viviani, Anatole France, and some other Academicians, speak French extremely well, but even these live in hope of improvement, of some day mastering the finest shades of nasality and cadence, the violet rays of rhythm.

MR. MASEFIELD, the poet, does not believe that war times nourish the arts. The human brain does its best work, he says, when men are happy. How perfectly true! Look at ancient Greece. She was continually at war, and what did the Grecians do for art? A few poets, a few philosophers and statesmen, a few sculptors, and the story is told. On the other hand, look at England in Shakespeare's time. The English people were inordinately happy, for there were no wars to depress them, barring a few little tiffs with the French and the Spanish, and one or two domestic brawls. The human brain does its best work when men are happy, indeed. There was Dante, a cheery old party. But why multiply instances?

HAVING read a third of H. M. Tomlinson's "The Sea and the Jungle," we pause to offer the uncritical opinion that this chap gets as good sea-water into his copy as Conrad, and that, in the item of English, he can write rings around Joseph.

LIKE others who have traversed delectable landscapes and recorded their impressions, in memory or in notebooks, we have tried to communicate to other minds the "incommunicable thrill of things": a pleasant if unsuccessful endeavor. When you are new at it, you ascribe your failure to want of skill, but you come to realize that skill will not help you very much. You will do well if you hold the reader's interest in your narrative: you will not, except by accident, make him see the thing you have seen, or experience the emotion you experienced.

So vivid a word painter as Tomlinson acknowledges that the chance rewards which make travel worth while are seldom matters that a reader would care to hear about, for they have no substance. "They are no matter. They are untranslatable from the time and place. Such fair things cannot be taken from the magic moment. They are not provender for notebooks."

HE quotes what the Indian said to the missionary who had been talking to him of heaven. "Is it like the land of the musk-ox in summer, when the mist is on the lakes, and the loon cries very often?" These lakes are not charted, and the Indian heard the loon's call in his memory; but we could not better describe the delectable lands through which we have roamed. "When the mist is on the lakes and the loon cries very often." What traveler can better that?

OLD Bill Taft pulled a good definition of a gentleman t'other day. A gentleman, said he, is a man who never hurts anyone's feelings unintentionally.

MR. GENEROUS is the claim agent for the New Haven railroad at New Britain, Conn., but a farmer whose cow wandered upon the rails tells us that he lost money by the settlement.

WILLIAM BENZINE, who lives near Rio, Wis., was filling his flivver tank by the light of a lantern when——— But need we continue?

OUR notion of a person of wide tastes is one who likes almost everything that isn't popular.

SPEAKING of the Naval Station, you may have forgotten the stirring ballad which we wrote about it during the war. If so—

YEO-HEAVE-HO!

It was a gallant farmer lad
    Enlisted in the navy.
"Give me," said he, "the deep blue sea,
    The ocean wide and wavy!"

A sailor's uniform he'd don,
    And never would he doff it.
He packed his grip, and soon was on
    His way to Captain Moffett.

In cap of white and coat of blue
    He labored for the nation,
A member of the salty crew
    That worked the Naval Station.

· He soon became the best of tars,
    A seaman more than able,
By sweeping streets, and driving cars,
    And waiting on the table.

He guarded gates, and shoveled snow,
    And worked upon the highway.
"*All* lads," said he, "should plough the sea,
    And would if I had *my* way."

Week-end he took a trolley car,
    And to the city hied him,
Alongside of another tar
    Who offered for to guide him.

The train rolled o'er a trestle high,
    The river ran below him.
"Well, I'll be blamed!" our tar exclaimed,
    And grabbed his pal to show him.

"Yes, dash my weeping eyes!" he cried.
    "That's water, sure, by gravy!
The first blue water I have spied
    Since joining of the navy!"

*   *   *   *   *

Now, "landsmen all," the moral's plain:
    Our navy still is arming,
And if you'd plough the well known main,
    You'd best begin by farming.

If you would head a tossing prow
　　Among our navigators,
Get up at morn and milk the cow,
　　And yeo-heave-ho the 'taters.

Do up your chores, and do 'em brown,
　　And learn to drive a flivver;
And some day, when you go to town,
　　You'll see the raging river.

THE speaker of the House of Commons, who, "trembling slightly with emotion," declared the sitting suspended, needs in his business the calm of the late Fred Hall. While Mr. Hall was city editor of this journal of civilization an irate subscriber came in and mixed it with a reporter. Mr. Hall approached the pair, who were rolling on the floor, and, peering near-sightedly at them, addressed the reporter: "Mr. Smith, when you have finished with this gentleman, there is a meeting at the Fourth Methodist church which I should like to have you cover."

IN his informing and stimulating collection of essays, "On Contemporary Literature," recently published, Mr. Stuart P. Sherman squanders an entire chapter on Theodore Dreiser. It seems to us that he might have covered the ground and saved most of his space by quoting a single sentence from Anatole France, who, referring to

Zola, wrote: "He has no taste, and I have come to believe that want of taste is that mysterious sin of which the Scripture speaks, the greatest of sins, the only one which will not be forgiven."

"WHAT is art?" asked jesting Pilate. And before he could beat it for his chariot someone answered: "Art is a pitcher that you can't pour anything out of."

IT IS much easier to die than it is to take a vacation. A man who is summoned to his last long voyage may set his house in order in an hour: a few words, written or dictated, will dispose of his possessions, and his heirs will gladly attend to the details. This done, he may fold his hands on his chest and depart this vexatious life in peace.

IT IS quite another matter to prepare for a few weeks away from town. There are bills to be paid; the iceman and the milkman and the laundryman must be choked off, and the daily paper restrained from littering the doorstep. There is hair to be cut, and teeth to be tinkered, and so on. In short, it takes days to stop the machinery of living for a fortnight, and days to start it going again. But, my dear, one must have a change.

JUST A REHEARSAL.

[From the Elgin News.]

Mr. and Mrs. Perce left immediately on a short honeymoon trip. The "real" honeymoon trip is soon to be made, into various parts of Virginia.

LAME IN BOTH REGISTERS?

[From the Decatur Review.]

Dr. O. E. Williams, who is conducting revival services in the First United Brethren church, spoke to a large audience on Friday night on "Lame in Both Feet." Mrs. Williams sang a solo in keeping with the sermon.

FLORAL POME.

(Sign on Ashland Ave.: "Vlk the Florist.")
For flowers fragrant, sweet as milk,
Be sure to call on Florist Vlk.

Roses, lilies, for the folks
Can be purchased down at Vlk's.

Of bouquets there is no lack
At the flower shop of Vlk.

Orchids, pansies, daisies, phlox,
All are sold at Florist Vlk's.

A wondrous place, a shop de luxe
Is this here store of William Vlk's.

F. E. C. Jr.

[229]

THE Boston aggregation, by the way (a witty New Yorker, a musician, informed us), is sometimes referred to as the Swiss Family Higginson and the Bocheton Symphony orchestra.

TOUCHING on musical criticism, a Chicago writer who visited St. Louis to report a music festival had a few drinks before the opening concert. His telegraphed review began: "Music is frozen architecture."

ASIDE from his super-mathematics, Dr. Einstein is understandable. He prefers Bach to Wagner, Shakespeare to Goethe, and he would rather walk in the valleys than climb the mountains.

THE SECOND POST.
[Example of pep and tact.]

Dear Sir: We absolutely cannot understand why you do not buy stock in the——— proposition or why we have not heard from you in reference to our letter. A man in your position should be able to invest some of his earnings into a proposition that should turn out a big success. It seems to us that the more rotten a proposition is the better the people will buy.

Now if you can explain this as to why the people bite on the many and poor schemes that are out to the public as there has been in the last six months, the information would be more than gladly received by us.

Let's get away from all this bunk stuff and think for ourselves and put your money in a real live proposition such as the —————.

After you invest your money in our business, do not fail to submit our proposition to some of your friends, so as to put this proposition over the top just as soon as possible.

May this letter act on you and try to improve your thought on investing your money with us, for we stand as true and honest as we can in order to make money for our clients.

Trusting that you will mail your check or money order to us at your very earliest convenience while the security is still selling at par, $10 per share, or a letter from you stating your reason for not doing so, we are, respectfully yours, etc.

In dedicating her autobiography to her husband, Mrs. Asquith quotes Epictetus: "Have you not received powers, to the limit of which you will bear all that befalls? Have you not received magnanimity? Have you not received courage? Have you not received endurance?" Mr. Christopher Morley thinks the gentleman needs them, but we are not so sure. It is said that when Margot mentioned to him the large sum she was to receive for the book, Mr. Asquith remarked, "I hope, my dear, that it isn't worth it."

As many know, Mr. Humphry Ward is a person of importance in his line. An American couple in London invited him to dine with them at their hotel, and concluded the invitation with the line, "If there is a Mrs. Ward, we should like to have her come, too."

In the Review of Reviews, Mr. Herbert Wade entitles his interview with Prof. Michelson, "Measuring the Suns of the Solar System." Wonder how he explained it to the Prof?

"She left a note saying she would do the next worst thing to suicide. . . . She went to Cleveland but decided to return."
Try South Bend.

"He decided that life was not worth living after that, so he came to South Bend."—South Bend Tribune.
Stet!

WHY THE DOG LEFT TOWN.
[From the Newton, Ia., News, Dec. 2.]

Warning—A resident of North Newton went home from work Saturday night and as he went in the front door a man went out the back door.

This party had better leave town, for I know who he is and am after him.   W. H. Miller.

[From the same paper, Dec. 5.]

I have since discovered that it was a neighbor's dog that bounded out of the back door as I came in the front door the other night.   My wife had gone to a neighbor's and left the back door ajar, hence a big dog had no trouble getting in.

W. H. Miller.

" 'I DON'T see why we go to England for nincompoops when we have men like Prof. Grummann here at home,' remarked Fred L. Haller." —Omaha Bee.

We trust Mr. Haller called up the Professor and explained what he meant.

THE PASSIONATE PURE FOOD EXPERT TO HIS LOVE.

Come live with me, my own pure love,
And we will all the pleasures prove,
In passion unadulterated
And bliss that isn't benzoated.

Love's purest formula we'll spell:
Our joys will never fail to jell.
The honeyed kisses we imprint
Will show of glucose not a hint.

[233]

Your Wiley will your food prepare,
And cook a meal to curl your hair;
And every morning you shall have a
Rare cup of genuine Mocha-Java.

And you shall have a buckwheat cake
Better than mother used to make,
And sirup from the maple wood—
Not a vile sorghum "just as good."

The eggs, the bacon, and the jam
Shall be as pure as Mary's lamb;
And nothing sans a pure-food label
Shall grace your matutinal table.

Oh, hearken to your Harvey's suit,
And 'ware the phony substitute.
If pure delights your mind may move,
Come live with me and be my Love.

PROF. BROWN of Carlton College complains that college faculties are concerned with the mental slacker and the laggard, that they have geared their machinery to the sluggard's pace. True enough, but not only true of educational institutions. In a democracy everything is geared to the pace of the weak.

"As for authors," sighs Shan Bullock, "their case is fairly hopeless. But I recognize that in the new democracy even average intellect has no place at present. The new democracy is on trial. Until it has proven definitely whether it sides with cinemas or ideals, there is not even a living for men who once held an honored place in the scheme of things. That is a dark saying, but I think it is true."

WE thought the doubtful honor was possessed by the United States, but M. Cambon declares that there is no other country where people take so little interest in foreign politics as they do in France.

A NERVY Frenchman, M. Bourgeois, has translated "The Playboy of the Western World." You can imagine with what success. "God help me, where'll I hide myself away and my long neck naked to the world?" becomes "Dieu m'aide, où vais-je me cacher et mon long cou tout nu?"

THE President of the Chicago Chapter of the Wild Flower Preservation Society wrote to the Department of Agriculture for a certain Bulletin on Forestry and another one on Mushrooms for the book table at their Exhibition in the Art Institute. In due time arrived 250 copies of "How to make unfermented grape juice" and 250 copies of "Hog Cholera." Anybody want them?

OH, DON'T YOU REMEMBER SWEET MARY, BEN BOLT?

"What has become of Mary MacLane?" asks a reader. We don't know, at this moment, but we remember—what is more important— a jingle by the late lamented Roz Field:

"She dwelt beside the untrodden ways,
    Among the hills of Butte,
A maid whom no one cared to love,
    And no one dared to shoot."

THE Montmartre crowd had a ticket in the Paris municipal election. The design on the carte d'electeur was a windmill, with the legend below, "Bien vivre et ne rien faire." This would do nicely for our city hall push.

Is there another person in this wicked world quite so virtuous as a chief of police on the day that he takes office?

INDIFFERENCE.

Said B. L. T. to F. P. A.,
"How shall I end the Line to-day?"
"It's immaterial to me,"
Said F. P. A. to B. L. T.   M. L. H.

LET it, then, go double.

Mr. Dubbe's Program Study Class.

(ACCOMPANYING THE SYMPHONY ORCHESTRA CONCERTS.)

Reported by Miss Poeta Pants.

I.—THE NEAPOLITAN SIXTH.

Mr. Criticus Flub-Dubbe's program study class began the season yesterday afternoon with every member present and keenly attentive. After a preparatory sketch of old Italian music, Mr. Dubbe told us about the Neapolitan Sixth, which, he said, had exercised so strong an influence on music that, if Naples had never done anything else, this alone would have insured to the city fame in history.

"The Neapolitan Sixth," said Mr. Dubbe, "is so called because the composers of the Neapolitan school of opera were the first to introduce it freely. D. and A. Scarlatti were at the head of the school and were well-known musicians. Bach, who was not so well known, also used this sixth."

"Which used it first?" asked Mrs. Givu A. Payne.

"Bach, of course," replied Mr. Dubbe. "Bach used everything first."

"Dear old Bach!" exclaimed Miss Georgiana Gush.

"The Neapolitan Sixth," continued Mr. Dubbe, "is usually found in the first inversion; hence the name, the sixth indicating the first inversion of the chord."

"How clever!" said Mrs. Gottem-Allbeat.

"It is an altered chord, the altered tone being the super-tonic. The real character of the chord is submediant of the subdominant key; that is, it is a major chord, and the use of such a major chord in the solemn minor tonalities is indicative of the superficiality of the Italian school—a desire for a change from the strict polyphonic music of the times. Even the stern Bach was influenced."

"The Italians are so frivolous," said Mrs. Boru-Stiffe.

"A reign of frivolity ensued," went on Mr. Dubbe. "Not only was Italian music influenced by this sixth, but Italian art, architecture, sculpture, even material products. Take, for example, Neapolitan ice-cream. Observe the influence of the sixth. The cream is made in three color tones —the vanilla being the subdominant, as the chord is of subdominant character; the strawberry being the submediant, and the restful green the lowered supertonic or altered tone."

"What is the pineapple ice?" asked Miss Gay Votte.

"The pineapple ice is the twelfth overtone," replied Mr. Dubbe.

"There doesn't seem to be anything that Mr.

Dubbe doesn't know," whispered Mrs. Fuller-Prunes to me with a smile.

I should say there wasn't!

After the lecture we had a lovely hand-made luncheon. Miss Ellenborough presided at the doughnuts and Mrs. G. Clef poured. It was such a helpful hour.

II.

"You remember," said Mr. Dubbe, "that Herr Weidig, in his lecture on the wood winds, gave a double bassoon illustration from Brahms' 'Chorale of St. Anthony,' which you are to hear to-day. But Herr Weidig neglected to mention the most interesting point in the illustration—that the abysmal-toned double bassoon calls attention to the devil-possessed swine, St. Anthony being the patron saint of swine-herds. I want you to listen carefully to this swine motive. It is really extraordinary." Mr. Dubbe wrote the motive on the blackboard and then played it on his double bassoon, which, he said, is one of the very few in this country.

"The bassoon," said Mr. Dubbe, "was Beethoven's favorite instrument. I go further than Beethoven in preferring the double bassoon. Among my unpublished manuscripts are several compositions for this instrument, and my concerto for two double bassoons is now in the hands of a Berlin publisher.

[239]

"But to recur to the Brahms chorale. You should know that it makes the second best variations in existence. The best are in the Heroic Symphony. The third best are Dvorák's in C major."

"C. Major—that's the man who wrote 'Dorothy Vernon,'" giggled Miss Vera Cilly.

"I am not discussing ragtime variations," said Mr. Dubbe, severely.

"Not knocking anybody," whispered Miss Gay Votte.

"Another interesting point in connection with this week's program," resumed Mr. Dubbe, "is the river motive in Smetana's symphonic poem, 'The Moldau.' Three flutes represent (loosely speaking; for, as I have often told you, music cannot represent anything) the rippling of the Moldau, a tributary of the Danube. If the composer had had a larger river in mind he would have used nine flutes. If this composition of Smetana's seems rather unmusical, allowance must be made for him, as the poor man was deaf and couldn't hear how bad his own music was."

"Wasn't Beethoven deaf?" asked Miss Sara Band.

"Only his physical ears were affected," replied Mr. Dubbe. "Smetana's soul ears were also deaf."

At the close of the lecture Miss Ellenborough

gave us a surprise in the way of raised doughnuts made in the form of a G clef. Mrs. Gottem-All-beat poured.

III.

There was an ominous flash in Dr. Dubbe's eye when he arose to address the class. "We have this week," he began, "a program barbarous enough to suit the lovers of ultra-modern music. There is Saint-Saëns' overture, 'Les Barbares,' to begin with. This is as barbaric as a Frenchman can get, and is interesting chiefly as a study of how not to use the trumpets. But for sheer barbarity commend me to Hausegger's 'Barbarossa.' Here we find the apotheosis of modern exaggeration. Hausegger strove to make up for inimportant themes by a profuse use of instruments. Only one theme, which occurs in the third movement, is of any account, and that is an imitation of an old German chorale. In this most monotonously muted of tone-poems the composer forgot to mute one instrument—his pen."

"My! but Dr. Dubbe is knocking to-day," whispered Miss Sara Band.

"The thing is in C major and opens with a C major chord," continued Dr. Dubbe. "That is the end of the C major; it never returns to that key. This is modern music. Take the third movement. It opens with a screeching barbershop chord. A little later ensues a prize fight between two themes, which continues until one of them is knocked out. In this edifying composition, also, snare drum sticks are used on the kettle drums. More modern music. Bah!"

I have never seen Dr. Dubbe so irritated.

"Let us turn to something more cheerful," resumed Dr. Dubbe; and seating himself at the piano he played the Schubert C minor impromptu. "On the second page," he said, "where the key becomes A flat major, occurs a harmony which looks and sounds like a foreign chord. Treated harmonically it is a second dominant formation, and should read C flat, D natural, A flat, diminished seventh of the key of the dominant. Schubert does not, however, use it harmonically, otherwise the B natural would read C flat. These notes are enharmonic because, though different, they sound the same."

"How clear!" exclaimed Miss Gay Votte.

"But Schubert, instead of progressing harmonically, goes directly back into the tonic of A flat major."

"How careless of him!" said Mrs. Givu A. Payne.

"Schubert uses it in its natural position. If the enharmonic C flat were used the chord would then be in its third inversion. Each diminished seventh harmony may resolve in sixteen different ways."

"Mercy!" murmured Mrs. Fuller-Prunes. "How much there is to know."

Dr. Dubbe passed his hand across his brow as if wearied. "I shall never cease to regret," he said, "that Schubert did not write C flat. It would have been so much clearer."

After the lecture Miss Ellenborough gave us another surprise—doughnuts made in the shape of flats. Dr. Dubbe ate five, saying that D flat major was his favorite key.

I rode down in the elevator with him and he repeated his remark that Schubert had unnecessarily bemuddled the chord.

"I am sure you made it very plain," I said. "We all understand it now."

"Do you, indeed?" he replied. "That's more than I do."

Of course he was jesting. He understands everything.

IV.

Dr. Dubbe was in his element yesterday. The trinity of B's—Bach, Beethoven, and Brahms— or, as Dr. Dubbe put it, the "trinity of logicians," was much to his taste: a truly Gothic program.

"But what a contrast is the second half," said Dr. Dubbe. "In the first we have the Kings of absolute music. In his youth Beethoven strayed from the path (for even he must sow his musical

[243]

wild oats), but in his maturer years he produced no music that was not absolute. But in the second half we have Berlioz and program music."

"I thought program music was music suitable for programs," said Mrs. Givu A. Payne.

"Berlioz," continued Dr. Dubbe, "instituted the 'musical reform' in Germany—the new German school of Liszt and Wagner. Berlioz's music is all on the surface, while Brahms' music sounds the depths. He uses the contra-bassoon in about all of his orchestral compositions (you will hear it to-day), and most of his piano works take the last A on the piano. If his bass seems at times muddy it is because he goes so deep that he stirs up the bottom."

"How clear!" exclaimed Miss Gay Votte.

"Take measure sixty-five in Berlioz's 'Dance of the Sylphs,'" said Dr. Dubbe. "The spirits hover over Faust, who has fallen asleep. The 'cellos are sawing away drowsily on their pedal point D (probably in sympathy with Faust), and what sounds like Herr Thomas tuning the orchestra is the lone A of the fifth. The absent third represents the sleep of Faust. This is a trick common to the new school. Wagner uses it in 'Siegfried,' in the close of the Tarnhelm motive, to illustrate the vanishing properties of the cap. In measure fifty-seven of the Ballet you will find a chord of the augmented five-six, a harmony

[244]

built on the first inversion of the diminished seventh of the key of the dominant, with lowered bass tone, and which in this instance resolves into the dominant triad. Others claim that this harmony is a dominant ninth with root omitted and lowered fifth."

"It has always seemed so to me," said Mrs. Fuller-Prunes. But I don't believe she knows a thing about it.

"I think it's all awfully cute," said Miss Georgiana Gush.

"The harmony," resumed Dr. Dubbe, frowning, "really sounds like a dominant seventh, and may be changed enharmonically into a dominant seventh and resolve into the Neapolitan sixth. This is all clear to you, I suppose?"

"Oh, yes," we all replied.

Dr. Dubbe then analyzed and played for us Brahms' First Symphony, after which Miss Ellenborough served doughnuts made in the shape of a Gothic B. We all had to eat them—one for Bach, one for Beethoven, and one for Brahms.

v.

Dr. Dubbe did not appear enthusiastic over this week's program. I guess because there was no Bach or Brahms on it. But we enjoyed his lecture just the same.

"Raff was the Raphael of music," said Dr.

Dubbe. "He was handicapped by a superabundance of ideas, but, unlike Raphael, he did not constantly repeat himself. This week we will have a look at his Fifth Symphony, entitled 'Lenore.' "

"Oh!" exclaimed Miss Georgiana Gush, "that's the one the hero of 'The First Violin' was always whistling."

"As you all know," said Dr. Dubbe, "this symphony is based on Bürger's well-known ballad of 'Lenore,' but as only the last movement is concerned with the actual ballad I will confine my remarks mainly to that. I wish, however, to call your attention to a curious harmony in the first movement. Upon the return of the first theme the trombones break in upon a dominant B major harmony with what is apparently a dominant C major harmony, D, F, and B. But the chords are actually enharmonic of D, E sharp, and B. This is a dominant harmony in F sharp. Listen for these trombone chords, and pay special attention to the E sharp—a tone that is extremely characteristic of Raff."

"I think I have read somewhere," said Mrs. Givu A. Payne, "that Raff was exceedingly fond of E sharp."

"He was," said Dr. Dubbe. "He often said he didn't see how he could get along without it. But to resume:

"The fourth movement opens with Lenore's

lamentation over her absent lover and her quarrel with her mother—the oboe being the girl and the bassoon her parent. Lenore foolishly curses her fate (tympani and triangle), and from that moment is lost. There is a knock at the door and her dead lover appears with a horse and suggests something in the nature of an elopement. Not knowing he is dead, Lenore acquiesces, and away they go (trumpets, flutes and clarinets).

" 'T is a wild and fearful night. Rack scuds across the moon's wan face (violas and second violins). Hanged men rattle in their chains upon the wayside gibbets (triangle and piccolo). But on, on, on go the lovers, one dead and the other nearly so.

"At last they reach the grave in the churchyard, and death claims the lost Lenore ('cellos and bass viols *pizzicato*). For a conclusion there is a coda founded on the line in the ballad, 'Gott sei der Seele gnädig.' It is very sad."

Dr. Dubbe seemed much affected by the sad tale, and many of us had to wipe tears away. But Miss Ellenborough came to our rescue with some lovely doughnuts made in the shape of a true lovers' knot. These, with the tea, quite restored us.

VI.

There really wasn't any study class this week—that is, Dr. Dubbe did not appear. While the

[247]

class waited for him and wondered if he were ill a messenger brought me the following note:

"MY DEAR POETA: Kindly inform the class that there will be no lecture this week. I cannot stand for such a trivial program as Herr Thomas has prepared. C. F.-D."

"He might have told us sooner," said Miss Georgiana Gush.

"Why, yes; he knew last week what the next program would be," said Mrs. Faran-Dole.

"The eccentricity of genius, my dear," remarked Mrs. Gottem-Allbeat. "Genius is not tied down by rules of conduct of any sort."

"Well," said Mrs. Givu A. Payne, "I don't blame him for not wanting to analyze this week's program. There isn't a bit of Bach or Brahms on it."

"Ladies," said Miss Ellenborough, coming forward with a gentleman who had just arrived, "let me introduce Mr. Booth Tarkington, of Indiana. Mr. Tarkington came up to attend the lecture, but as Dr. Dubbe will not be here Mr. Tarkington has kindly consented to give a doughnut recital, so to speak."

"Oh, how lovely!" we all exclaimed.

"Mr. Tarkington," added Miss Ellenborough, "is well known as the author of the Beaucaire doughnut, the pride of Indiana doughnutdom."

[248]

Saying which Miss Ellenborough removed the screen that conceals her work table and Mr. Tarkington, in an incredibly short time, produced a batch of Beaucaires. They were really excellent, and we didn't leave a single one. Mr. Everham Chumpleigh Keats poured.

After tea we all adjourned to the concert, which we enjoyed immensely, in spite of the absence of Bach and Brahms. Not knocking Dr. Dubbe.

A LINE-O'-TYPE OR TWO

Inveniat, quod quisque velit; non omnibus unum est, Quod placet; hic spinas colligit, ille rosas.
—*Petronius.*

THE PASSING OF SUMMER.

*S*UMMER *is gone with its roses,*
  Summer is gone with its wine;
Likewise a lot of dam choses
  Not so ideal and benign.

King Sol is visiting Virgo,
  On his Zodiacal way.
'Morrow's the twenty-third! Ergo,
  Summer will vanish to-day.

SUMMER in town is a synonym for dullness. The theaters offer nothing of importance; only trivialities are to be found on "the trestles." Musical directors appeal only to the ears—chiefly the long ears mentioned by Mozart. Bookstores offer "best sellers," "the latest fiction," and "books worth reading" on the same counter; and the magazines become even less consequential. Art in all its manifestations matches our garments for thinness and lightness.

During the canicular period intellectual activity

[251]

is at a stand, and we should be grateful for the accident which tilted earth's axis at its present angle; for when the leaves begin to fly before the "breath of Autumn's being" we plunge into the new season with a cleared mentality and a great appetite for things both new and old.

A MAN asks the Legal Friend of the People, "Will you kindly publish whether or not it is illegal for second cousins to marry in the state of Illinois?" and the Friend replies, "No." Aw, go on and publish it. There's no harm in telling him.

WHYNOTT?

[From the Boston Globe.]

From this date, Sept. 25, 1920, I will not be responsible for any bill contracted by my wife, Mrs. Bernardine Whynott.   G. Whynott.

IN all the world the two most fragile things are a lover's vows and the gut in a tennis racket. Neither is guaranteed to last an hour.

IT would help along the economic readjustment, suggests Dean Johnson, of New York University's school of commerce, if we all set fire to our Liberty Bonds. We can't go along with the Dean so far, but we have a hundred shares of copper stock that we will contribute to a community bonfire.

THE height of patriotism, confides P. H. T., is represented by Mr. Aleshire, president of the Chicago Board of Underwriters, who, billed to deliver a patriotic address in an Evanston theater, paid his way into the theater to hear himself talk.

IT MUST BE ABOUT TIME.

Sir: The Federal Reserve bank at New Orleans has received a letter from a patriot who wants to know where and when he shall pay the interest on his Liberty bond.   ROCKY.

"IN fact, I've finished—would you say a sonnet?"—concludes H. G. H., to whom we recommend the remark of James Stephens: "Nobody is interested in the making of sonnets, not even poets."

REFERRING to the persons who are given to the making of sonnets, Norman Douglas wrote: "I have a sneaking fondness for some of the worst of these bards. . . . And it is by no means a despicable class of folks who perpetrate such stuff; the third rate sonneteer, a priori, is a gentleman, and this is more than can be said of some of our crude fiction writers who have never yielded themselves to the chastening discipline of verse composition, nor warmed their hearts, for a single instant, at the altar of some generous ideal."

[253]

THE trouble with minor poets is well set forth by Conrad Aiken in The Dial, who refers to the conclusions of M. Nicolas Kostyleff after a tentative study of the mechanism of poetic inspiration: "An important part in poetic creation, he maintains, is an automatic verbal discharge, along chains of association, set in motion by a chance occurrence."

POETRY.
(Lord Dunsany.)

What is it to hate poetry? It is to have no little dreams and fancies, no holy memories of golden days, to be unmoved by serene midsummer evenings or dawn over wild lands, singing or sunshine, little tales told by the fire a long while since, glow-worms and briar rose; for of all these things and more is poetry made. It is to be cut off forever from the fellowship of great men that are gone; to see men and women without their halos and the world without its glory; to miss the meaning lurking behind the common things, like elves hiding in flowers; it is to beat one's hands all day against the gates of Fairyland and to find that they are shut and the country empty and its kings gone hence.

WHY is it that in nearly all decisions of the Supreme court the most interesting opinions are delivered by the dissenting justices?

"NEW Jack-a-Bean dining room furniture, used two months; will sell cheap."—El Paso Herald.

That is the kind that Louis Canns has his apartment furnished with.

A CHANGE FROM LATIN ROOTS.
[From the Reedsburg, Wis., Free Press.]

Miss Edna White resumed her school duties after a week's vacation for potato digging.

OUR FAVORITE AUTUMN POEM.
(By a New Jersey poetess.)

Autumn is more beautiful, I think,
    Than Spring or Winter are.
For then trees change at the river's brink—
    How beautiful they are.

I love to see the different colors so bright—
    That grow around brooks & grottoes.
Leaves that are pressed are a pleasant sight
    To make photograph frames & mottoes.

DR. JOHNSON or somebody said that a surgical operation was necessary to get a joke into a Scotchman's head; but the Glasgow Herald, reporting the existence of a London detective named Leonard Jolly Death, conjectures that it was probably an ancestor of his who was drowned in the butt of Malmsey wine.

ONE is usually mistaken in such matters, but we visualize Mr. Imer Pett, general manager of the Bingham Mines, in Salt Lake City, as quite otherwise.

THE SECOND POST.

[Received by a wholesale grocery house, from an Italian customer.]

Gentlemen: My wife wants me to suggest that you observe one of our Italian customs by remembering her with a bit of Christmas cheer. As she is the only wife I got I trust you will help me keep her.   JOE.

DENTAL FLOSS.

Sir: D. Seiver is a dentist on Kedzie avenue. If I were a complete contrib, I might head this, "Now, this isn't going to hurt a bit," but, as I am not, I merely proceed to nominate C. O. Soots, of North Salem, Ind., as chief chimney sweep to the Academy, and propose the Rev. Ed. V. Belles of the First Presbyterian Church of Northville, Mich., to ring in the new for the members. As a substitute for Mr. D. Seiver, you might induce the nominating committee to accept Dr. J. Byron Ache, a dentist of Uniontown, Pa.

BALLYSLOUGHGUTTERY.

[256]

THE melancholy days have come
For him who's naturally glum:
But for the man whose liver's right
These Autumn days are pure delight.

"COMPLAINS He Was Called Sexagenarian—
Candidate Says Many Voters Thought It Had
to Do With Sex."—Boston Herald.
Flattered, but unappreciative.

LADY GODIVA writes from Loz Onglaze:
"Have been having wonderful weather. Quite
warm yesterday, the first of December. Riding
around with just my fur cape on."

SOME people hold potatoes for higher prices,
while others, like Scribner's Sons, hold sets of
Henry James' novels at $130, an increase of $82
over the original price.

JUST ABOUT.

Sir: How long do you suppose the Snow Ball
Laundry will last in Quinter, Kansas? The proprietor is G. W. Burns.   P. V. W.

IN an almanack, which is printed once a year,
or in a dictionary or encyclopedia, which is re-
published after ten or twenty years, you would
expect to find fewer errors than in a daily newspaper; but apparently time has little to do with

it. Consulting the Britannica's article on Anatole France, we were inexpressibly shocked to find therein the atrocities, "L'Ile des Penguins" and "Maurice Bàrrès."

WE were looking through the France sketch to see whether there was mention of a story he wrote before he became well known, entitled "Marguerite." A Paris publisher found it recently in a magazine and asked M. France to write a preface to it, that it might be issued as a book. Quoth France: "It would be an excess of literary vanity on my part to resurrect the story. But my vanity would, perhaps, be greater were I to try to suppress it."

REFERENCE books, as is well known, improve like wine with age, and the efficiency of our proof room is to be accounted for, in part, by the vintage volumes that line its library shelf. There are sixty of these rare old tomes, and five of them are useful; these being, we think, first editions. There is a Who's Who of the last century that is still in good condition, and the dictionary of biography with which Lippincotts began business. Bibliophiles would, we believe, enjoy looking over the shelf.

JAW JINGLES.

If a Hottentot taught a Hottentot tot
  To talk ere the tot could totter,
Ought the Hottentot tot be taught to say "ought,"
  Or "naught," or what ought to be taught her?

If to hoot and to toot a Hottentot tot
  Be taught by a Hottentot tutor,
Ought the Hottentot tutor get hot if the tot
  Hoot and toot at the Hottentot tutor?

G. B.

"NATURE NEVER DID DECEIVE . . ."

No sooner had blundering man accomplished
the ruin of Halifax than Mother Nature sent a
blizzard with a foot or two of snow. A kindly
dame—as kindly as the old lady of Endor. She
has her gentle, her amorous moods, in which we
adore her, and write ballads to her beauty; but
we know, if we are wise, that her beauty is "all
in your eye," to speak in the way of science, not
of slang, and that she is savage as a jungle cat.
Like some women and much medicine, she should
be well shaken before taken, and always one must
keep an eye upon Nature, or one may feel her
claws in one's back. So we have reflected on a
summer's day in woods; but the forest seemed not
less beautiful, nor was our meditation melancholy.
To be saddened by the inescapable is a great mistake.

NO. 68, COUNTING FROM LEFT TO RIGHT.

[From the Goshen, Ind., Democrat.]

Albert E. Compton, 68, a former well known Elkhart taxi driver, went to California last summer and told his friends he was going into the movies. A communication from him yesterday informed them of his appearance in a mob scene.

MRS. FRED L. OLSON is on the programme to sing vocal selections."—Portland Telegram.

That's the trouble. They will sing them.

OUR young friend who is about to become a colyumist might lead off with the jape about the switchman who asked for red oil for his lantern. Then there is that side-stitching sign, "Pants pressed, 10 cents a leg, seats free."

COMMERCIAL CANDOR.

Sir: A tailor in Denver advertises: "If your clothes don't fit we make them."   W. V. R.

HEARD, by R. M., in a department store: Shoe-polish demonstrator: "And if you haven't already ruined your shoes with other cleaners this will do the work."

FAREWELL!
(By Poeta.)

Comet, Comet, shining bright
In the spaces of the night,
Every hour swinging higher
From the Sun of thy desire;
Astral vagrant, stellar rover,
Dipping under, dipping over
Path of Venus, Earth, and Mars
Till there's naught beyond but stars;
Cutting, in thy lane elliptic,
Thro' the plane of the ecliptic,
Far beyond pale Neptune's track—
Good-by, Comet! Hurry back!

AN UNCOMMONLY HAPPY THOUGHT.
(A. J. Balfour, Letter to Mary Gladstone, 1891.)

"It is unfortunate, considering that enthusiasm
moves the world, that so few enthusiasts can be
trusted to speak the truth."

THE SECOND POST.
[The editor of the Winneconne, Wis., Local to his flock.]

Dear Subscriber: You probably know that the
Local editor and his wife have been away from
Winneconne most of the time during the last ten
months. Every month we expected to get back
again. The suspense was somewhat hard. During the meantime Mrs. Flanagan, each week,

would worry and talk about the paper as much as ever. The doctor desired to have it off her mind. During the meantime she did not want the plant closed for even a short time. Now it has been decided to take a holiday vacation, during which time Mr. and Mrs. Flanagan will release themselves from all business cares and build up in health. No doubt, you will realize the delicate situation of the affair, and bear with us in the matter until the Local again resumes its regular publication dates, for surely both of us are very much attached to the paper, the town, and its people, and the surrounding country.

M. C. FLANAGAN.

THE DAY OF "DON'TS."

Thanksgiving was a holiday I welcomed when a boy,
But now it is a solemn feast without a jot of joy.
It used to be a pleasure to attack the toothsome turkey,
But now when I approach the bird I'm anything but
    perky.

A multitude of dismal "Don'ts" impair my appetite;
A fear of what may happen me accompanies each bite.
There hovers round this holiday a heavy cloud of dread
That never lifts till I am safe, with water-bag, in bed.

I used to drink a glass of wine, but that is bad, I'm told,
So now I ship in water—just as much as I can hold.

To fail to fletcherize my food were fatal, without ques-
    tion;
I never touch the stuffing, as it taxes the digestion.

When the lugubrious feast is done I hasten from my chair
To open all the windows wide, and let in lots of air;
And then I sit around an hour and chew a wad of gum
Until the fullness disappears from my distended tum.

That pleasant, dozy feeling I compel myself to shake,
For should I venture on a nap I'd never, never wake;
And if I sneeze I take alarm and hasten out of doors,
To start a circulation in my poison-clotted pores.

The fact that I am still alive is due, I'm glad to say,
To heeding all the dinner "Don'ts" that went with
    yesterday.
It was, from soup to raisins, by and large, and all in all,
The solemnest Thanksgiving meal that ever I recall.

A BALANCED TUITION.

Sir: The fourth grade teacher in Roland, Ia.,
is Viola Grindem. Fortunately for the kids the
high school principal is Cora Clement.   T. B.

"We wish the coöperative factories a success,"
says an esteemed contemporary on our left. So
do we, with this prediction, that if success is
achieved it will be by the same methods that are
employed in the iniquitous capitalistic system.

ALTHOUGH the name topic bores us to distinction, as a young lady of our acquaintance puts it, we should feel we were posing if we neglected to find room for the following:

Sir: Deedonk, can you provide a chaise longue in the Romance language department of the Academy for George E. Ahwee of Colon, Panama?   RUSTY.

WE knew what was meant, and yet it gave us a slight start to read in a Minnesota paper, "Pickle your own feet while they are cheap and clean."

OPINION CONCURRED IN.

Sir: My heart with pleasure filled when I saw that Riquarius quoted it as I always want to do, "with rapture fills." While I realized it is the height of presumption to think I could improve on Wordsworth, don't you agree with me that rapture is more expressive than pleasure?

JAY AYE.

"Rapture" might be preferred for another reason: the accent falls on a stronger syllable. Suppose George Meredith had used "pleasure" in his lines—

> "Lasting, too,
> For souls not lent in usury,
> The rapture of the forward view."

Every good poet has left lines that could be bettered for another ear. Probably Wordsworth leads the list.

TRANSCENDENTAL CALM.

Sir: Remember the story about Theodore Parker and Emerson? While they were walking in Concord a Seventh Day Adventist rushed up to them and said, "Gentlemen, the world is coming to an end." Parker said, "That doesn't affect me; I live in Boston." Emerson said, "Very well. I can get along without it."   E. H. R.

So the President has been converted to universal military training—as a war measure. Better late than never, as Noah remarked to the Zebra, which had understood that passengers arrived in alphabetical order.

THIS REFERS, OF COURSE, TO FRANCE.

[From Faguet's "Cult of Incompetence."]

Democracy has the greatest inducement to elect representatives who are representative, who, in the first place, resemble it as closely as possible, who, in the second place, have no individuality of their own, who, finally, having no fortune of their own, have no sort of independence. We deplore that democracy surrenders itself to politicians, but from its own point of view, a point of view which it cannot avoid taking up, it is absolutely right. What is a politician? He is a man who, in respect of his personal opinions, is a nullity, in respect of education a mediocrity; he shares the general sentiments and passions of the crowds, his sole occupation is politics, and if that career were closed to him he would die of starvation. He is precisely the thing of which democracy has need. He will never be led away by his education to develop ideas of his own; and, having no ideas of his own, he will not allow them to enter into conflict with his prejudices. His prejudices will be, at first, by a feeble sort of conviction, afterward, by reason of his own interest, identical with those of the crowd; and lastly, his poverty and the impossibility of his getting a living outside of politics make it certain that he will never break out of the narrow circle where his political employers have confined him; his imperative mandate is the material necessity which obliges him to obey; his imperative mandate is his inability to quarrel with his bread and butter. Democracy obviously has need of politicians, has need of nothing else but politicians, and has need indeed that there shall be in politics nothing else but politicians.

AN IOWA ROMANCE.

[From the Clinton Herald.]

Lost—A large white tom cat with gray tail and two gray spots on body. Return to 1306 So. Third street and receive reward.

Lost—"Topsy" black persian cat. Any one having seen her kindly call 231 5th ave.

WE SHOULD LIKE TO KNOW WHAT HAPPENED.

[From the Idaho Falls Register.]

A lady's leather handbag left in my car while parked on Park avenue two weeks ago. Owner can have same by calling at my office, proving the property and paying for this ad. If she will explain to my wife that I had nothing to do with its being there, I will pay for the ad.

C. G. Keller.

COME INTO THE GARDEN, MAUD.

[From the Tavares, Fla., Herald.]

The home of Mr. and Mrs. H. H. Duncan was the center of attraction Sunday afternoon. All the relatives and a few special friends were there to celebrate two happy occasions, the anniversary of Mr. and Mrs. Duncan's marriage and the marriage of Miss Cora L. Peet, Mrs. Duncan's sister, to Mr. J. E. Hammond, and the soft winds of March had blown the planet of love over this beautiful home.

[267]

The composition of the decorations adhered with striking fidelity to nature. The wide veranda was completely screened in by wild smilax and fragrant honeysuckle vines, which entwisted themselves among the branches of sweet myrtle and native palms, fitly transforming it into a typical Arcadian scene beckoning to

"Come unto the garden, Maud;
  I am here at the gate alone;
And the woodbine spices are wafted abroad,
  And the muck of the rose is blown."

Soon the sound of music greeted the impatient ear. With a voice full of individuality of flavor and unusual quality, Mr. Carl E. Duncan, perfectly accompanied by his mother at the pianoforte, rendered "I Hear You Calling Me." Then the coming of the bridal couple was heralded by the solemn tones of Mendelssohn's wedding march. Never was a bride more beautiful; never——

[Well, hardly ever.]

AND HOW CALM THE OCEAN IS!

[Correspondence from Florida.]

I've fallen in love with the salt water bathing. It feels wonderfully refreshing here, below the equator.

POEMS YOU MAY HAVE MISSED.

BETWEEN THE BARN AND THE WOODHOUSE.

Between the barn and the woodhouse,
  Where oft old Jersey would stand,
I remember 'twas on this self-same spot
  Where she kicked Elizabeth Ann.

I could hear the clang of the bucket,
  And also poor Annie's refrain,
And when the family reached her,
  She was writhing and groaning with pain.

Mother stooped down to caress her
  As she lay there stunned on the ground,
And our big, simple minded brother
  Thought he should examine the wound.

Without halt or hesitation,
  He dropped to his knees in the dirt;
Although she lay stunned and bleeding,
  He asked her where she was hurt.

Then Annie, in a half sitting posture,
  While resting on mother's arm,
Feebly responded to brother,
  "Between the woodhouse and barn."

W. T. N.

"THE Chicago convention left the Democratic party as the sole custodian of the honor of the country."—Orator Cummings.

Some custodian, *nous en informerons l'univers!*

To the inspired compositor and proof reader of the York, Neb., News-Times he is General Denuncio.

"THE plebicide showed an overwhelming majority in favor of King Constantine's return."— St. Paul Pioneer Press.
Very good word.

WE were not alone in financing the war. An income tax payment of $14,000,000 was made in New York yesterday. The identity of the individual is not disclosed, but the painstaking Associated Press says that "he is obviously one of the richest men in the United States."

"THINKING as One Walks."—Doc Evans.
"Meaning," conjectures Fenton, "that if one is bow-legged one is likely to think in circles." Or if one limps, one is likely to come to a lame conclusion. Or if— Roll your own.

THE PHILOSOPHY OF BALDNESS.

One by one the hairs are graying,
One by one they blanch and fall;
Never stopping, never staying—
W. t. h. and d. i. all!   *W. R.*

A DEAD SHOT.

[From the Mt. Carmel, Ill., Republican.]

The Mount Carmel Gun club held its weekly shoot this afternoon, the chief feature being the demonstration of expert marksmanship by Mr. Killam of the Du Pont Powder Co.

IT WOULD PUT 'EM ON THE STAGE.

Why does not some pianist give us a really popular recital programme? Frezzample:

> Moonlight Sonata.
> The Harmonious Blacksmith.
> Mendelssohn's Spring Song.

> Old Favorites:
> Recollections of Home.
> Silvery Waves.
> Monastery Bells.
> Etincelles.
> Waves of the Ocean.
> Gottschalk's Last Hope.

> Clayton's Grand March.
> The Battle of Prague.
> The Awakening of the Lion.

THERE is an encouraging growth of musical understanding and appreciation in this country. Even now you hear very many people say, "I liked the scherzo."

[271]

"HE sat down in a vacant chair," relates a magazine fictionist. It is, everything considered, the safest way. Much of the discord in the world has been caused by gentlemen—and ladies as well—who sat down in chairs already occupied.

A KENWOOD pastor has resigned because some members of his flock thought him too broad. The others, we venture, thought him too long.

"PROF. HOBBS Will Make Globe Trot."— Michigan Daily.
Giddap, old top!

Vacation Travels.

IT IS a great pleasure to be free, for a time, from the practice of expressing opinion; free to read the newspapers with no thought of commenting on the contents; free to glance at a few hectic headlines, and then bite into a book that you have meant to get to for a long time past, to read it slowly, without skipping, to read over an especially well done page and to put the book aside and meditate on the moral which it pointed, or left you to point. Unless obliged to, why should anybody write when he can read instead? One's own opinions (hastily formed and lacking even the graces of expression) are of small account; certainly they are of less account than Mr. Mill's observations on Liberty, which I have put down in order to pen a few longish paragraphs. (I would rather be reading, you understand; my pen is running for the same reason some street cars run—to hold the franchise.) And speaking of Mill, do you remember the library catalogue which contained the consecutive items, "Mill on Liberty" and "Ditto on the Floss"?

One can get through a good many books on a long railway journey. My slender stock was exhausted before I reached Colorado, and I am compelled to re-read until such time as I can lay in a fresh supply. At home it is difficult to find time to read—that is, considerable stretches of time, so that one may really digest the pages which he is leisurely taking in. Fifty years ago there were not many more books worth reading than there are to-day, but there was more time to assimilate them. A comparatively few books thoroughly assimilated gave us Lincoln's Gettysburg address. Not long ago my friend the Librarian was speaking of this short classic. "Did you ever," said he, "read Edward Everett's address at Gettysburg?" "No," said I, "and I fear I shall never get to it." "It is stowed away among his collected orations," said he. "Not half bad. Unfortunately for its fame, Mr. Lincoln happened along with a few well chosen remarks which the world has preferred to remember."

———

Another advantage of a long railway journey is the opportunity it affords to give one's vocal cords a (usually) well-merited rest. It is possible to travel across the continent without saying a word. A nod or a shake of the head suffices in your dealings with the porter; and you learn nothing from questioning him, as he has not been on that run before. Also, business with the train and Pullman conductors may be transacted in silence, and there is no profit in asking the latter to exchange your upper berth for a lower, as he has already been entreated by all the other occupants of uppers. When the train halts you do not have to ask, "What place is this?"—you may find out by looking at the large sign on the station. Nor is it necessary to inquire, "Are we on time?"— your watch and time-table will enlighten you. You do not have to exclaim, when a fresh locomotive is violently attached, "Well, I see we got an engine"—there is always somebody to say it for you. And you write your orders in the dining car. There is, of course, the chance of being accosted in the club car, but since this went dry the danger has been slight. And conversation can always be averted by absorption in a book, or, in a crisis, by pretending to be dumb.

Not everybody can travel three or four days without exchanging words with a fellow traveler. Mr. George Moore, for example, would be quite wretched. Conversation is the breath of his being, he says somewhere. I understand that Mr. Moore has another book on press, entitled "Avowals." Avowals! My dear! . . . After the "Confessions" and the "Memoirs" what in the world is there left for the man to avow?

What a delightful fictionist is Moore! And never more delightful than when he is writing fiction under the appearance of fact. No one has taken more to heart the axiom that the imaginary is the only real. As my friend the Librarian observed, the difference between George Moore and Baron Munchausen is that Moore's lies are interesting.

Travelers must carry their own reading matter under government ownership. The club car library now consists of time-tables, maps, and pamphlets setting forth the never to be forgotten attractions of the show places along the way. These are all written by the celebrated prose poet Ibid, and, with a bottle of pseudo beer or lemon pop, help to make the club car as gay a place as a mortician's parlor on a rainy afternoon.

The treeless plateau over which the train rolls, hour after hour, is the result of a great uplift. It was not sudden; it was slow but sure. This result is arid and plateautudinous, in a manner of speaking—not the best manner. It makes me think of democracy—and prohibition. To this complexion we shall come at last. To be sure, the genius of man will continue to cut channels in the monotonous plain; erosion will relieve the dreary prospect with form and color, but it bids fair to be, for the most part, a flat and dry world, from which many of us will part with a minimum of regret. There will remain the inextinguishable desire to learn what wonders science will disclose. Perhaps—who knows?—they will discover how to ventilate a sleeping car.

At Albuquerque I remarked a line of Mexicans basking in the sun (having, perhaps, finished jumping on their mothers). They looked happy —as happy as the Russian peasants used to be. Men who know Russia tell me that the peasants really were happy, even under the twin despotisms of Vodka and Czar. It was not, of course, a reformer's idea of happiness: a reformer's idea of happiness is perpetual attention to everybody's business but his own. People who are interested academically in other people's happiness usually succeed in making everybody unhappy. Now, the Russian's happiness was a poor thing, but his own. In reality he was wretched and oppressed, and his voice and bearing should have expressed his misery and hopelessness, instead of a foolish content and a silly detachment from political affairs. But he is at last emancipated, and, as was said of Mary's fleecy companion, now contemplate the condemned thing!

Liberty, equality, international amity, democracy, the kingdom of heaven on earth—All that is very well, yet Candide remarked to Dr. Pan-

gloss when all was said and done, "Let us culti-
vate our garden."

———

There are so many interesting things along the
way that I should, I suppose, be filling a notebook.
But why mar the pleasure of a journey by taking
notes? as the good Sylvestre Bonnard inquired.
Lovers who truly love do not keep a diary of their
happiness.

———

In Phoenix, Arizona, distance lends enchant-
ment to the view. But the hills are far away, and
as I did not visit the Southwest to contemplate the
works of man, however ingenious, I followed the
westering sun to where the mountains come down
to the sea. I do not fancy the elevated parts of
New Mexico and Arizona; and as there was no
thought of pleasing me when they were created, I
feel free to express a modified rapture in their
contemplation. I should have remembered
enough geology to know that granite is not found
in this section, except at the bottom of the Grand
Canyon. The hills I like are made of old-fash-
ioned stuff, not young upstart tufa and sandstone
that was not thought of when the Laurentians
were built. One really cannot have much respect
for a rock that he can kick to pieces. The gay
young buttes in this land of quickly shifting hori-
zons are not without their charm; they look well

in certain lights, and they are decidedly better than no hills at all. Although immature, they have an air of pretending to be very ancient, to be the ruins of mountains. They are picturesque and colorful. And I would swap a league of them for one archaic boulder the size of a box-car, with a thick coverlet of reindeer moss.

———

When I left the train at Pasadena I saw what I took to be a procession of the K. K. K. It proved to be citizens in flu masks. I was interested, but not alarmed; whereas a lady tourist who debarked on the following day fell in a swoon and was conveyed to the hospital. The newspapers charged her disorder to the masks, but as she was from Chicago I suspect that her reason was unsettled by the sudden revealment of a clean city. And Pasadena is clean—almost immaculate. I was obliged to join the masqueraders, and I found the inconvenience only slight. The mask keeps the nose warm after sundown, and is convenient to sneeze into. And I have never remarked better looking folks than the people of Pasadena. The so-called human race has never appeared to better advantage. The women were especially charming, and were all, for once, equally handicapped, like the veiled sex in the Orient.

———

Whoever christened it the Pacific ocean was the giver of innocent pleasure to every third person who has set eyes on it since. "There's the Pacific!" you hear people exclaim to one another when the train reaches the top of a pass. "Isn't it calm! That's why it is called the Pacific. And it is pacific, isn't it?" Some such observation must have escaped the stout adventurer in Darien, before he fell silent upon his peak.

———

I shall say nothing about the never to be sufficiently esteemed climate of California, nor even allude to the windjammers of Loz Onglaze. The last word concerning those enthusiasts was spoken by a San Francisco man who, addressing the people of "Los," explained how the city might overcome the slight handicap imposed by its distance from the sea. "Lay an iron pipe to tidewater," he advised; "and then, if you can suck as hard as you can blow, you will presently have the ocean at your doors." It would be difficult to improve on that criticism. And so, instead of praising the climate, I will gladly testify that it is easier to live in this part of the country than anywhere east of the Sierras. And San Diego impresses me as the easiest place in the state to live, the year round.

———

The mechanical effort of existence is reduced to its minimum in La Jolla, a suburb of San Diego, where I am opposing a holiday indolence to pen these desultory lines. "There's lots of good fish in the sea" that beats against this rockbound but not stern coast, and there is a fish market in the village. But each day I see the sign in the window, "No fish." The fisherman, I am told, is "very independent," a euphemism for tired, perhaps. He casts his hooks and nets only when the spirit moves him, and is not impelled to the sea by sordid motives. A true fisherman, I thought, though he never change his window sign.

To-day's newspapers contain the protest of the governor of Lower California against the proposed annexing of his territory by the United States. Señor Cantu may be a hairless dog in the manger; he may, as he claims, represent the seething patriotism of all but a negligible percentage of the population; but he is no doubt correct in merely asserting that the peninsula will not be annexed. Incidentally, he is on sure ground when he attributes the chaos in Mexican affairs to "conflicting political criteria." It is all of that. So far as I have casually discovered, there is no active annexation sentiment on this side of the border, for there is no hope of overcoming that provision in the Mexican constitution which makes it a matter of high treason to encourage a movement for the diminution of Mexican territory.

———

Gov. Cantu's phrase, "conflicting political criteria," applies rather happily to the doings in Paris these days. The Peace conference and prohibition in the United States are perhaps the two most prominent topics before the public, and they are the two things which I have not heard mentioned since I began my travels.

A LINE-O'-TYPE OR TWO

"Lord, what fools these mortals be."

COUNTRY LIFE IN AMERICA.

SING high the air like dry champagne,
  The fields of virgin snow!
(Sing low the mile-hike from the train,
  In five or ten below.)

Sing high the joys the gods allot
  To our suburban state!
(Sing low the dinner gone to pot,
  Because the train is late.)

Sing high the white-arched woodland way,
  Resembling faëry halls!
(Sing low the drifts that stay and stay,
  In which your motor stalls.)

Sing high, sing low, sing jack and game,
  Sing Winter's spangled gown!
(Let him who will these things acclaim—
  I'm moving in to town.)

SCRATCH a man who really enjoys zero
weather, and you will find blubber.

[283]

BORN in Sioux City, to Mr. and Mrs. Matt Hoss, a daughter. Who'll contribute a buggy?

"FOR SALE—1920 Mormon chummy."—Minneapolis Journal.

Five-passenger at least.

THERE WERE IMMORTALS BEFORE JET WIMP.

Sir: In the Lowell (Mass.) Daily Journal and Courier, dated Feb. 4, 1853, I find the following: "What's in a name! The name of the superintendent of the Cincinnati Hospital is Queer Absalom Death." Thus showing that there were candidates for the Academy seventy years ago.   CONCORD.

SOME sort of jape or jingle might be chiseled from the fact that Lot Spry and Ida Smart were married t'other day in Vinton, Ia.

CONTRIBUTIONS THAT HAVE AMUSED US.

Proprietor of hotel in Keokuk, answering call from room: "Hello!"

Voice: "We are in Room 30 and now ready to come down."

Prop.: "Take the elevator down."

Voice: "Is the elevator ready?"

[Proprietor sends bellboy to Room 30 to escort newly-wedded couple to terra firma.]

"WEDS 104th Veteran."—Springfield Republican.

The first hundred veterans are the hardest.

FOR official announcer in the Academy, E. K. proposes James Hollerup of Endeavor, Wis.

SHE PREFERRED HER PSYCHOPATHY STRAIGHT.

Sir: At a party last night one of my sex read the recent buffoonery, "Heliogabalus," by the Smart Set editors. When the reader reached the choice second act one of the women (the bobbed hair type) refused to listen to any more of the "salacious rot," and walked over to the bookcase, from which, after careful study, she picked out Krafft-Ebing's Psychopathia Sexualis. I ask you, ain't women funny?   PHILARDEE.

No, not in this instance. We quite sympathize with the lady. We much prefer Havelock Ellis to "Jurgen," for example. Chacun à son goût.

THIS peculiar and unliterary preference of ours may be due to the fact that once upon a time, in a country job-print, we were obliged to read the proofs of a great many medical works, made up largely of "Case 1, a young man of 28," "Case 2, a woman of thirty," etc. These things were instructive, and sometimes interesting. But when "Case 1" is expanded to a novel of three or four hundred pages, or "Case 2" expressed in the form of hectic vers libre, a feeling of lassitude comes o'er us which is more or less akin to pain.

THE COME-BACK.

Click! Click!
Goes my typewriter,
Transcribing letters
That the Boss dictates around
His chew
After he has discussed the weather,
And the squeak in his car,
And his young hopeful's latest,
And the L. of N.

Click! Click!
While he writes impudent
Things
For the Line
About the Stenos,
And asks me how to spell
The words.

Hark!
To the death rattle of
The cuspidor
Upset,
As he departs at two o'clock
To golf,
While I type on
Till five.   AGNES.

MR. GOMPERS advises labor to accomplish its desires at the polls, instead of chasing after the red gods of political theory. This is excellently gomped, and will make as deep an impression as an autumn leaf falling on a rock.

SINCE the so-called working classes are unable or unwilling to do so simple a sum as dividing the total wealth of a nation by the number of its inhabitants; since they cannot or will not understand that if the profits of an industry are exceeded by the wages paid, the industry must stop; since they only reason *a posteriori* when that is well kicked, and by themselves—it is fortunate that the United States has the opportunity to watch the progress of the experiment now making in England.

NOWADAYS the buying and dispatching of Christmas gifts is scientifically made. One merely selects this or that and orders it sent to So-and So. One turns in to a book store a list of titles and a list of names and addresses, and the book store does the rest.

Consequently one misses the pleasant labor of tying up the gift, of journeying to the post-office, to have it weighed and stamped, and of dropping it through the slot and wondering whether the string will break, or whether the package will go astray.

WE were engaged in dropping newly-minted double-eagles into the Christmas stockings of our contributors when an auto truck got mired near our chamber window, and the roar of it woke us up.

JAPANESE, Chinese, Hindus, and other Orientals are disliked, not because of race or color, but because they are willing to work. Anyone who is willing to work in these times is, like the needy knife-grinder, a wretch whom no sense of wrongs can rouse to vengeance.

WASHLADIES get more money for less work than any other members of the leisure class, with the exception of the persons who work on putting greens. In addition to their wage, they get carfare and two or three meals. Why? Because it is not generally known that a mere man, with a washing machine and a bucket of solution, can do more washing in three hours than a washlady does in three days.

WHAT do they mean "industrial unrest"? Industry never rested so frequently or for such protracted periods.

THE natives of Salvador can neither read nor write, but their happy days are numbered. The Baptist church is going to spend three millions on their conversion. Their capacity for resistance is not so great as that of the Chinese. Do you remember what Henry Ward Beecher said of the Chinese? "We have clubbed them, stoned them, burned their houses, and murdered some of them, yet they refuse to be converted. I do not know any way except to blow them up with nitroglycerine, if we are ever to get them to heaven."

"Do you not know," writes Persephone, "that with the coming of all this water, all imagination and adventure have fled the world?" Just what we were thinking t'other evening, when we dissipated a few hours with our good gossip the Doctor. "I am," said he, pouring out a meditative three-fingers, "in favor of prohibition; and I believe that some substitute for this stuff will be found."

We pursued that lane of thought a while, until it debouched into a desert. The Doctor then took down the works of Byron, and read aloud— touching the high spots in "English Bards and Scotch Reviewers," "Don Juan," "Childe Harold," "The Prisoner of Chillon"—pausing ever and anon to replenish the glasses. It was midnight ere the book was returned to its shelf.

It was a delightful evening. And we wondered whether, without the excellent bourbon and the cigars, we should not have had enough of Byron by 10:30.

AN English publisher binds all his books in red because, having watched women choosing books in the libraries, he found that they looked first at the red-bound ones. Does that coincide with your experience, my dear?

OUR interest in Mr. Wells' "Outline of History" has been practically ruined by learning from a geologist that Mr. Wells' story of creation is frightfully out of date. Should he not have given another twenty-four hours to so large an opus?

VISITING English authors have a delightful trick of diagramming their literary allusions. Only the few are irritated by it.

"AND as I am in no sense a lecturer . . ."— Mr. Chesterton.
Seemingly the knowledge of one's limitations as a public entertainer does not preclude one from accepting a fee five or ten times larger than one would receive in London. We are languidly curieux de savoir how far the American equivalent would get in the English capital.

You cannot "make Chicago literary" by moving the magazine market to that city. Authors lay the scenes of their stories in New York rather than in Chicago, because readers prefer to have the scene New York, just as English readers prefer London to Manchester or Liverpool. If a story is unusually interesting it is of no consequence where the scene is laid, but most stories are only so-so and have to borrow interest from geography.

THANKS TO MISS MONROE'S MAGAZINE.

Only a little while ago
The pallid poet had no show—
No gallery that he could use
To hang the product of his muse.

But now his sketches deck the walls
Of many hospitable halls,
And juries solemnly debate
The merits of the candidate.

TRADE CLASSICS.

EVERY trade has at least one classic. One in the newspaper trade concerns the reporter who was sent to do a wedding, and returned to say that there was no story, as the bridegroom failed to show up. Will a few other trades acquaint us with their classics? It should make an interesting collection.

Sir: The classic of the teaching trade: A school teacher saw a man on the car whose face was vaguely familiar. "I beg your pardon," she said, "but aren't you the father of two of my children?"   S. B.

Sir: The son of his father on a certain occasion, when the paper was overset, objected to adding two pages, but in a moment of economical inspiration agreed to permit one extra page.

C. D.

Sir: Don't forget the classic of dry stories. "An Irishman and a Scotchman stood before a bar—and the Irishman didn't have any money."

L. A. H.

To continue, the Scotchman said: "Well, Pat, what are we going to have to-day? Rain or snow?"

Sir: "If you can't read, ask the grocer." But I heard it differently. An Englishman and an American read the sign. The American laughed. The Englishman did not see the humor of it. The American asked him to read it again; whereupon the Englishman laughed and said: "Oh, yes; the grocer might be out."   3-STAR.

YOU may know the trade classic about the exchange editor. The new owner of the newspaper asked who that man was in the corner. "The exchange editor," he was informed. "Well, fire him," said he. "All he seems to do is sit there and read all day."

DIVERS correspondents advise us that the trade classics we have been printing are old stuff. Yes; that is the peculiar thing about a classic. Extraordinary, when you come to think of it.

"TIMERIO," which is simpler than Esperanto, "will enable citizens of all nations to understand one another, provided they can read and write." The inventor has found that 7,006 figures are enough to express any imaginable idea. But we should think that a picture book would be simpler.

"You can go to any hotel porter in the world," says the perpetrator of Timerio, "and make yourself understood by simply handing him a slip of paper written in my new language." But you can do as well with a picture of a trunk and a few gestures. The only universal language that is worth a hoot is the French phrase "comme ça."

DENATURED LIMERICKS.

There was a young man of Constantinople,
Who used to buy eggs at 35 cents the dozen.
   When his father said, "Well,
   This is certainly surprising!"
The young man put on his second best waistcoat.

"THE maddest man in Arizona," postcards J. U. H., who has got that far, "was the one who found, after ten miles' hard drive from his hotel, that he had picked up the Gideon Bible instead of his Blue Book." Still, they are both guide books, and they might be interestingly compared.

To one gadder who asked for a small coffee, the waitress in the rural hotel said, "A nickel is as small as we've got." Some people try to take advantage of the bucolic innkeeper.

"I HAVE not read American literature; I know only Poe," confesses M. Maeterlinck. Well, that is a good start. For a long time the only French author we knew was Victor Hugo. Live and learn, say we.

"HE is so funny with the patisserie," says Mme. Maeterlinck of M. Charles Chaplin. "He is an artist the way he throw the pie." Is he not? M. Chaplin is to Americans what the Discus Thrower was to the Greeks.

SINGS, in a manner of singing, Mr. Lindsay in the London Mercury:

"I brag and chant of Bryan, Bryan, Bryan,
    Candidate for President who sketched a silver Zion."

But we prefer, as simpler and more emotional, the classic containing the lines—

> "But my soul is cryin'
> For old Bill Bryan."

YOU are familiar with the cryptic inscription "TAM HTAB," which ceases to be cryptic when you turn the mat over; but did you ever hear about the woman who christened her child "Nosmo King," having been taken by those names on two glass doors which stood open?

A CHIPPEWA FALLS advertiser offers for sale "six Leghorn roosters and one mahogany settee." And we are requested to ascertain whether the settee is a Rhode Island Red or a Brown Leghorn.

A ROTARY club is being formed in the Academy by the Rev. Rodney Roundy of the American Missionary Association.

WHAT do you mean "prosperity"? Even the Nonquit Spinning Co. of New Bedford has shut down.

JOSEPH CONRAD's latest yarn is the essence of romance. But what is romance? For years we have sought a definition in ten words; but while romance is easily recognized, it is with difficulty defined. Walter Raleigh came the nearest to it in a recent essay. "Romance," said he, "is a love

[295]

affair in other than domestic surroundings." This would seem also to be the opinion of a West Virginia editor, who, reporting a marriage, noted that "the couple were made man and wife while sitting in a buggy, and this fact rendered somewhat of a romantic aspect to the wedding."

MY LOVE, DID YOU KNOW THERE WERE SO MANY KINDS OF MAIDS?

[From the Derbyshire Advertiser.]

Mrs. Reeves requires—Cooks, £18 to £50, with Kitchenmaids, Scullerymaids, Betweenmaids, and Single-handed; Upper, Single-handed, Second, Under Parlourmaids £14 to £40; Head, Single-handed, Equal, First, Second, Third, Fourth, Fifth and Under Housemaids, good wages; Ladies' Maids, Useful Maids, Maid-Attendants, Maids, Housemaids, House-Sewingmaids, £18 to £30; Chambermaids, Housemaids, Stillroommaids, Pantry-maids, Cooks, £20 to £52; Kitchenmaids, £12 to £30; Staffmaids, Hallmaids, etc.

A YARN about a clean Turk reminded W. D. W. of a story that came straight from Gallipoli; and in running over the files of the Line we happened on it. Some British officers were arguing as to which had the stronger odor, the regimental goat or a Turk. It was agreed to submit the matter to a practical test, with the Colonel as referee. The goat was brought in, whereupon the Colonel fainted. A Turk was then brought in, whereupon the goat fainted.

As confirming that goat and Turk story, the following extract from a British soldier's letter, explaining the retreat before Bagdad, is submitted:

"We had been pursuing the Turks for several weeks, and victory was within our grasp, when the wind changed."

As a variant for "loophound," may we suggest "prominent hound about town"?

THE Isle of Yap, the Isle of Yap,
    Where burning Sappho never sung!
You ain't so much upon the map,
    But Uncle Samuel murmurs, "Stung!"

"AFTER submitting a contribution, how long must one remain in suspense?" asks E. L. W. That, sir, depends, as has been well said. But you would be safe in assuming, after, say, three months, that the contribution has been mislaid.

THE SECOND POST.
[Result of a collection letter that drew a sum on account.]

"Don't get peevish about this. I have a wife and large family. More coming."

[297]

HEARD in the Fort Des Moines Hotel: "Call for Mrs. Rugg! Call for Mrs. Rugg! Is she on the floor?"

YES, SOMETIMES WE THROW THE WHOLE MAIL AWAY WITHOUT LOOKING AT IT.

[From the Madison State Journal.]

It isn't "B. L. T." and "F. P. A." that makes the respective columns of these most celebrated of the "conductors" great. It is their daily mail. It comes to them in great bags. They open enough letters to fill that day's column, and consign thousands, unopened, to the waste basket. There is a fortune to some newspaper syndicate in the unopened mail of "B.L.T." and "F.P.A."

A LIMOUSINE delegate from the Federated Order of Line Scribes has waited on us to present the demands of the organization, among which are (1) recognition of the union; (2) appointing a time and place for meeting with a business committee to determine on a system of collective bargaining for Line material; (3) allowing the Order to have a voice in the management of the column. A prompt compliance with the demands of the Order failing, a strike vote will be ordered.

We have never limited the output of a contributor; the union will. No matter how excellent the idea, no matter how inspired the contrib

[298]

may be to amplify it, he will not be permitted to do more than a certain amount of work per day. However brilliant he may be, he will be held down to the level of the most pedestrian performer. In unionizing, moreover, he will be only exchanging one tyrant for another, and perhaps not so benevolent a one. Now, then, go to it, as the emperor said to the gladiators.

ALL RIGHT, DAISY.

Dear B. L. T., pray take this hint:
I shrink to see my name in print,
The agate line—O please!—for me.
I sign myself just—

DAISY B.

THE SHY AND LOWLYS.

I'm modest and meek,
And not a bit pushing.
Please set in Antique,
Or 14 point Cushing.

IRIS.

HE MIGHT TRIM THE VIOLETS.

Sir: Could you find an inconspicuous job around the Academy for a bashful man like Mr. Jess Mee, whom we had the pleasure of encountering in Toulon, Ill.?

[299]

We welcome Mr. Mark Sullivan, who fights the high cost of existence by turning his clothes inside out, to our recently established league, The Order of the Turning Worm. Mr. Sullivan, meet Mr. Facing-Both-Ways.

MR. MARK SULLIVAN may be interested in this case: "My husband," relates a reader, "did a job of turning for a man reputed to be wealthy. He removed the shingles from a roof, and turned all except those which were impossible: these few were replaced by new ones. The last I heard about this man he was said to have refused Liberty loan salesmen to solicit in his factory."

FIVE years ago a neighbor told us that he had his clothes turned after a season or two of wear, but we neglected to ask him how he shifted the buttonholes to the proper side. Left-handed buttoning would be rather awkward, especially if one were in a hurry.

MISS FORSYTHE of the Trades Union league explains that young women in domestic service feel there is a social stigma attached to the work. It is this stigmatism, no doubt, that causes them to break so many dishes. Anyway, Stigma is a lovely name for a maid, just as pretty as Hilda.

"WHY care for grammar as long as we are good?" inquired Artemus Ward. A question to be matched by that of the superintendent of Cook county's schools, "Why shouldn't a man say 'It's me' and 'It don't'?" Why not, indeed! How absurd was Prof. McCoosh of Princeton, who, having answered "It's me" to a student inquiry, "Who's there?" retreated because of his mortification for not having said "It's I." Silly old duffer! He would not have enjoyed Joseph Conrad, who uses unblushingly the locution, "except you and I."

No, let the school children, like them (or like they) of Rheims, cry out, "That's him!" *Usus loquendi* has made that as mellifluous as "that's me." It don't make you writhe, do it? Besides, we are all sinners, like McCoosh. And as a gentleman writes to the Scott County, Ind., Journal, "Let he that is without fault cast the first stone."

"I WANT to use the 'lightning-bug' verse," writes Ursus. "Please reprint it and say to whom credit should be given."

It is easier to reprint the lines than to locate the credit, but we have always associated them with Eugene Ware. They go—

"The lightning-bug is brilliant, but he hasn't any mind;
He stumbles through existence with his headlight on behind."

THE Harmony Cafeteria advertises, "Eat the Harmony Way." A gentleman who lunched there yesterday counted eighteen sword-swallowers.

REMINDFUL of the bow-legged floorwalker who said, "Walk this way, madam."

WATCHING the play, "At the Villa Rose," our thoughts wandered back to "Prince Otto," in which piece we first saw Otis Skinner. And we wondered precisely what George Moore means when he says that Stevenson is all right except when he tries to tell a story. According to Moore, a story is not a story if it keeps you up half the night; "it is only the insignificant book that cannot be laid down," he once maintained.

WHAT is a story? To us it is drama first, operating on character. To Conrad it is character first, being operated on by drama. That may be why we prefer "The Wrecker" to "The Rescue."

WRITES M. G. M. from Denver: "Madame Pompadour, late of Chicago, opened a beauty shop here, and one of our up-to-date young ladies asked her if she was doing the hair in the crime wave so popular in Chicago."

TRADE ADIEUS.

Sir: After I had entertained a saleslady all evening and had said good-night at her abode, she murmured, "Thanks! Will that be all?"

C. H. S.

ACCORDING to Dr. Kumm of the Royal British Geographical Society, the natives of Uganda are happier than we. So are the camels of Sahara. But hoonel, as Orpheus asked Eurydice, wants to be a camel?

Adventures of Robinson Crusoe.

BEING A FEW HITHERTO UNPUBLISHED PAGES FROM HIS JOURNAL.

I.

IN this, the seven and twentieth year of my captivity, I have been much distressed by the monotony of my existence. My habitation is as complete as I can wish; I have all the clothing to my need; and my subjects—my man Friday and his father, and the Spaniard—keep me abundantly supplied with food. When I was alone the necessity of husbandry gave me plenty to do, but now I am oppressed by a great lack of matter for occupation, both physical and mental. Questioning myself, I put the blame upon an evil state of mind into which I have fallen, in no longer finding profit in reading my bible and other books, or in meditating on this life and that which is to come.

I am rich in that I want for no material thing; and I am idle, in that I do naught to profit myself or my companions; so that, although practically a solitary, I am, as you might say, an idle rich class, and were I multiplied by thousands I should be a grievous burden on society.

Friday, perceiving the state of my mind, has set himself to entertain me, and, being an ingenious fellow, will no doubt succeed. As a beginning he took unto himself the management of our simple meals, and he has contrived so to expand them, both in quantity of food and time spent in consuming it, that a large part of my day is now given over to eating. I drink a great deal of wine with my meals, and of rum also, a great store of which I saved from the wreck; and these strong waters, added to the great quantity of food consumed, produce in me a pleasant torpor, which I find to be a satisfactory substitute for meditation.

II.

My man Friday came running to me this afternoon to relate that "many great number" of savages were landed on our shore, and that, by the preparations the wretches were making, a great feast was intended. The news was extremely welcome, for I have become so bored by the monotony of existence that any pretext for going abroad after nightfall is a godsend. So after disposing of a heavy dinner, that included six kinds of wines and liquors, my carriage, as I called it (though it was no more than a litter), was fetched by Friday and his father; and followed by the Spaniard, carrying my cloak and perspective glass, I set out for a little wooded hill that overlooked the beach on which the savages were encamped.

The dreadful wretches had finished their inhuman feast and were squatting on the sand, watching one of their number, a comely female, who was dancing wildly in a circle of strong firelight. The body of this creature was swathed in veils, which she removed, one after the other, until she was wholly naked. This degrading spectacle seemed to be enormously enjoyed by the spectators, who were grouped in the form of a horseshoe. I observed, also, that they were decorated with feathers and glass beads, and that, except for these ornaments, were as naked as the dancer.

My Spaniard, a God fearing man, was greatly shocked by the sight, and my man Friday, too, was strongly affected; but to my shame I must confess that I did not share their abhorrence. Yet even my stomach began to protest when the dancer, darting to one of the canoes, appeared with a gory head that had been chopped from one of the victims of the feast, and continued her shocking gyrations, to a most infernal din of barbarous musical instruments that half a hundred of the wretches were beating. The Spaniard and Friday urged, in their indignation, that we discharge our muskets at the unholy crew; but I restrained them from such an intelligible piece of violence, reflecting that the barbarous customs of these people might be regarded as their own disaster, and that I was not called upon to judge

[307]

their actions, much less to execute the judgment of heaven upon them. Besides, they were in such numbers that, had we attacked, we should have been overwhelmed. So, calling for my litter, I returned to my habitation.

A LINE-O'-TYPE OR TWO

Hew to the Line, let the quips fall where they may.

An artist friend, back from the Land of Taos, brings word of another artist who is achieving influence by raising hogs—or "picture buyers," as he sardonically calls them. This set us to wondering what had become of Arthur Dove, one of the first of the Einstein school to exhibit in this town. Despairing of the public intelligence, Mr. Dove took up the raising of chickens, and very old readers of this column may recall the verses in which we celebrated his withdrawal from art:

THE BROODING DOVE.

Arthur Dove is raising chickens,
   He has put his paints away:
Tell me, Chronos, where the dickens
   Are the Cubes of yesterday!

Dove was real, Dove was earnest,
   But his efforts came to nix.
Bowing to decree the sternest,
   He has gone to raising chicks.

[309]

There's a strong demand for broilers,
  There's a call for chicken-pie;
Dove declined to paint pot-boilers,
  So he put his brushes by.

Luck attend his every setting!
  May his inspirations hatch!
And, whatever price he's getting,
  May he market every batch.

"Perpetual reduction of my audience is my hobby," observes Mr. Yeats, who aspires to be the Einstein of song. When only twelve disciples are able to understand him, he will be content.

A scientific expedition will hunt for the missing link in Asia, and may find it. But it will never be known whether the m. l. was capable of the popular songs which one sees in the windows of music stores, or whether it could have done something better.

The gadder contrib who uses the Gideon Bible to hold the shaving mirror at the right angle is properly rebuked by sundry readers. As one of them, M. B. C., says, he may make the Line, but he'll have a close shave if he makes heaven.

We imagine the Gideon Bible is read more than may be supposed. Evening in a small town must be desperately dull to many travelers. And there are better love stories in the Bible than can be bought on the trains. Some of our gadding contribs have so good a writing style that we feel sure it must have been influenced by the Great Book.

A STERN PEDAGOGUE.

[From the Antelope, Montana, local.]

Miss Gladys Spank arrived here from Bozeman last Saturday and is again teaching in the school near Williams.

OUR esteemed contemporaries, F. P. A., Don Marquis, and Chris Morley, have taken the pains to reply to Miss Amy Lowell's recent remark that "colyums" are "ghastly and pitiful." Dear! dear! What has happened to their sense of humor?

SHE NOT ONLY HAS A BOOK. SHE HAS TWO!

"I wish to buy a book for a young lady," infoed the blond mustached one to a clerk at McClurg's. "She has both the 'Rubaiyat' and 'A Tale of Two Cities.' What do you advise?"   O. B. W.

"I NEVER could get to Detour, either," communicates Jezebel, "but recently, on a train, I passed through Derail, which seems to be a fairly thriving village, although some of the houses need paint."

☞ *Old readers detour here—*

YES, YES.

Sir: Herbert F. Antunes is a piano tuner in Evanston. **L. L. B.**

☞ *Resume main pike.*

YE STUFF.

Sir: "Yee Laundry" reads the sign over Yee Hing's washee at Deming, N. M. Wherein ye olde world is joined with ye olde English.

C. P. A.

"HENRY FORD is poverty stricken intellectually, morally, and spiritually." — Comrade Spargo.

Hint for Briggs: "Wonder what Henry Ford thinks about?"

POWELL'S taxicab service in Polo, Ill., offers "a rattle with every ride," and for the life of us we can't imagine the kind of car employed.

SPEAKING of Detour and Derail, "I wonder," wonders A. T., "whether in your travels you ever got to Goslow."

DATED.

Sir: From the Blue Book: "Pleasant View. Saloon on left corner. Turn left. Then follow winding road." A. C.

YOU KNOW THE TUNE.

"NO GIRL," say the rules of Northwestern University, "must walk the campus after dusk, unless to the library or to lectures, or for purposes of learning."

> *I'm a merry little campus maid,*
> *The campus sward I rove,*
> *Picking Greek roots all the day*
> *And learning how to love.*

CONSIDERING "A Treasury of English Prose," —prose that rivals great poetry—Mr. J. C. Squire came to an interesting conclusion—that "there is an established, an inevitable, manner into which an Englishman will rise when his ideas and images lift into grandeur; the style of the Authorized Version."

AUGUSTE COMTE listed five hundred and fifty-eight men and women who could be considered great in the history of the world. An English writer, striking from the list names that he had never heard of before, arrives at the "astounding fact" that since the dawn of history fewer than three hundred and fifty great men have lived. We too are astounded. We had no notion there were so many.

"GREAT BRITAIN," says Lloyd George, "must be freed of ignorance, insobriety, penury, and the tyranny of man over man." That ought not to require more than three or four glacial periods.

THE Woman's Club asks for "jingles for the jaw." Well, here are two from C. L. Edson. Try them on your jaw:

THE TREE TOADS.

A tree toad loved a she toad
   That lived up in a tree;
She was a three-toed tree toad,
   But a two-toed toad was he.

The two-toed tree toad tried to win
   The she toad's friendly nod;
For the two-toed tree toad loved the ground
   That the three-toed tree toad trod.

But vainly the two-toed tree toad tried—
   He couldn't please her whim;
In her tree toad bower
With her V-toe power,
   The she toad vetoed him.

[314]

THE RIDER AND THE ADDER.

Miss Tudor was a rider in a famous circus show;
For a pet she had an adder—and the adder loved her
 so!

She fed the adder dodder. It's a plant that lives on air,
Could you find an odder fodder if you hunted everywhere?

Miss Tudor bought some madder. It's a color rather
 rare,
And it made the adder shudder when Miss Tudor dyed
 her hair.

Her hair was soft as eider when she tried her madder dye;
Then, it had an odder odor—and was redder than the
 sky.

The adder couldn't chide 'er. It could only idle stare,
But a sadder adder eyed 'er when the rider dyed 'er hair.

ONE of our readers was dozing in the lobby of
a Boston hotel when he was aroused by an alter-
cation near the cigar stand. A was wagering B
that the name of the heroine of "The Scarlet
Letter" was Hester Thorne, B maintaining that
it was Hester Prim. The manager of the hotel
was about to call the police, forgetting that there
were none, when the gum-chewing divinity behind
the case awarded the decision to B, and the crowd
reluctantly dispersed.

WE have on hand a column of favorite wheezes sent in response to our invitation, and the only reason we have not printed them is the preponderance of our own stuff. Naturally, or not, we are better amused by the wheezes of contributors. Frexample the following evoked a smile:

"On the train running into Tulsa," wrote a gadder, "a native was fooling with the roller curtain, when suddenly it flew up with a snap. He looked bewildered, stuck his head out of the window, and finally said to himself, 'Well, I reckon that's the last they'll see of *that* derned thing!'"

As we have been informed, and as we repeat for the benefit of the School of Journalism, there is nothing to running a column except the knack of writing more or less apt headlines. And so for the instruction of students whose ambition may be vaulting in that direction we will reopen a short court in head-writing. See what you can do with the divorce suit of Hazel Nutt against John P. Nutt, filed in a Florida court.

As to the divorce suit of Hazel Nutt vs. John P. Nutt, M. M. C. offers, "Shucks!"

ANOTHER happy headline for the Nutt vs. Nutt divorce suit, suggested by Battle Creek: "Two Nutts Will Soon Be Loose."

THE hand-painted baby-blue pencil for the best headline last week goes to the artist on the San Francisco Chronicle for the following:

"Prehistoric Skulls Found Digging Wells."

WE see by the paper—our favorite medium of information—that Duluth is to have an evening of "wrestling and dance." A keen eye can probably tell the difference.

THE drawn-work decanter, prize for the best headline for the Nutt vs. Nutt divorce case, is awarded to G. C. H. for his inspiration, "Nutts for the Lawyers."

LIMERIK.

There was a young man from Art Creek
Who went around dressed in Batik.
    When they asked, "Are you well?"
    He replied, "Ain't it hell?
But in Art it's the very last shriek."

RECEIVED by a Missouri teacher: "Please excuse Frank for being absent. I kneaded him at home." In the woodshed? Ouch, Maw!

HOW could the teacher rebuke Emil when she read this excuse from his father? "The only excuse I have for Emil being late was nine o'clock came sooner than we expected."

[317]

FOR our part, we are moved to protest against the growing practice among parents of rebuking their children for playing with the children of prohibitionists. We should not visit upon the little ones the sins of their intemperate progenitors.

"ATTENTION, Members!" postcards the house committee of the Chicago Real Estate Board. "Get your feet under the table and you are putting your shoulder behind your board." This is another good reducing exercise.

WITH the return of the railroads to private control, we look for an immediate improvement in the service. For, as the dining-car waiter said, when requested to brush the crumbs from a table: "We's workin' for the government now. We don't have to brush no crumbs off no more." Well, he'll brush some crumbs off some more now, or he'll be fired.

ONE may send "harmless live animals" by parcel post, with the chances eight to five that the animal will be reduced to pulp or die of old age.

THE CHIGGER.

When the enterprising chigger is a-chigging
And maturing his felonious little plan,
He loves to climb the lingerie and rigging
And tunnel into Annabel and Ann.

The chigger then with chloroform they smother,
   His little hour of pleasure then is o'er,
So take this consideration with the other,
   A chigger's life is pretty much a bore.

A VERSATILE CHAP.

[From the Turton, S. D., Trumpet.]

Victor LaBrie gave several fine selections on the piano. Victor is a splendid musician. When he plays he has full control of the piano, and has splendid harmony to his selections.

Victor LaBrie started dragging Monday afternoon. He used the tractor and stated that it worked up fine.

"SEEING is believing," says the vender of a piano player. But perhaps you would prefer auricular evidence.

"THE only fad I have had for the last twenty-six years is my husband."—Mrs. Harding.

This is one of the very few really worthy fads that women have ever taken up.

ACT II., SCENE II.

JULIET.

What's in a name? That which we call a rose
By any other name would smell as sweet.

ROMEO.

Thou sayest a mouthful, love. And yet how
   come

[319]

That Myra Tinkelpaugh, of Cobleskill,
New York, conducts therein The Music Shop?

MR. SINK having resigned as plumber to the
Immortals, we are recommending in his place the
plumbing firm of Jamin & Jerkin, of St. Petersburg, Fla.

"BUY a communication ticket," advises a restaurant. This, understands E. S., gives you the
privilege of talking with the waitresses.

"EVERY American man has a mental picture of
his wife standing behind the door with a rolling-
pin."—Blasco Ibanez.

We fear the gifted Spaniard has acquired an
idea of American domestic life from Mr. Tom
Powers' sketches and other back-page comics.

A READER wonders what we can find in a book
so childishly egotistical as Margot Asquith's
Autobiography. Answer: much that is interesting. When we read an autobiography we are interested in the people written about rather than
in the writer. There are exceptions, of course;
for example, Henry Adams and Jacques Casa-
nova.

[320]

THE JANITOR ENTERTAINS.

[Iowa City Item.]

An unusual function for men in business circles was that which John Voelkel, janitor of the First National bank, supervised, Saturday evening. He gave a dinner, card party and a smoker to all the officers of the bank. Invitations were issued to every member of the staff, from president to clerk, and those who assembled at the custodian's home made merry for several hours at an event probably without a duplicate in banking history in Iowa City.

VARIANT OF THE V. H. W.

Sir: Please send me a copy of the famous valve handle wheeze. I have heard so much about it. I hope this reaches you before your limited supply is exhausted.   O. G. C.

P. S.—One of the fellows in the office just told me the joke, so you need not bother to send me a copy.   O. G. C.

CRUELLE ET INSOLITE.

[Transfer slip, Peninsular Railway Co.]

This ticket is good for one continuous passage only in the direction shown by conductor's punch in the face hereof.

[321]

HIGH, LOW, JACK, AND THE GAME.

Sir: While visiting in a New England family I accused them of being "highbrows," and they gave me these modern synonyms for highbrow and lowbrow, taken from a Boston paper:

Highbrow: Browning, anthropology, economics, Bacon, the string quartette, the uplift, inherent sin, Gibbon, fourth dimension, Euripides, "eyether," pâté de fois gras, lemon phosphate, Henry Cabot Lodge, Woodrow Wilson.

Low-highbrow: Municipal government, Kipling, socialism, Shakespeare, politics, Thackeray, taxation, golf, grand opera, bridge, chicken à la Maryland, "eether," stocks and bonds, gin rickey, Theodore Roosevelt, chewing gum in private.

High-lowbrow: Musical comedy, euchre, baseball, moving pictures, small steak medium, whisky, Robert W. Chambers, purple socks, chewing gum with friends.

Lowbrow: Laura Jean Libbey, ham sandwich, haven't came, pitch, I and her, melodrama, hair oil, the Duchess, beer, George M. Cohan, red flannels, toothpicks, Bathhouse John, chewing gum in public.   E. S.

A BACHELOR complains to us that prohibition has ruined his life. His companions have deserted their haunts—all, all are gone, the old familiar faces—and he can find no one to talk

to; and he talks very well, too. Now, we have
as much compassion for him as it is possible to
have for any bachelor, and yet we do not esteem
his case utterly hopeless. As Mr. Lardner has
suggested, when he repairs to his hotel at night he
can open the clothespress and talk to his other suit
of clothes.

TOLSTOI'S "Power of Darkness" reminds P. G.
Wodehouse of a definition of Greek tragedy—
the sort of drama in which one character comes to
another and says, "If *you* don't kill mother, *I*
will!"

"THE jehu of the rubber-neck wagon," reports
a gadder from Loz Onglaze, "called out: 'We
are now in the center of the old aristocratic center. That palatial residence on our left is the
home of Fatty Arbuckle.'"

MORNING IN IOWA.

A cold, rough, gloomy morning!
'Gainst yellow dawn the smoke
Of neighbors' chimneys stains the air,
Reminding me that yon grim, white-capped cone,
Which like a second Rainier stands in my back-
                    yard,
Like him of ash and cinders built, now calls
For more upbuilding. That white bloom
Which last night's snow hath left upon

[323]

His smooth and awful sides must now
Be sicklied o'er with more and yet more
Ashes.

What's that I smell—buckwheats?
And What's-his-name's pig sausage?
It is? Aha!
Gee, what a peach of a morning!

ABD-EL-KADER.

AN EVENING WITH SHAKESPEARE.

Sir: Overheard at the Studebaker: "What's put him off his nut?" Lady, answering: "He ain't really bugs—it's a stall. The old guy [Polonius] thinks he's got something on him."

P. S. D.

YOURS, ETC.

Sir: The height of efficiency is attained by Mervin L. Lane, Insurance Service, New York, who prints on his letterhead, "Unnecessary terms of politeness as well as assurances of self-evident esteem are omitted from our letters."

E. A. D.

"IT costs 30,000 Lenin rubles a day for food alone," says Prof. Zeidler of Viborg, referring to so-called life in Russia. Apparently, then, Lenin has not yet succeeded in making money utterly worthless.

[324]

HE OUGHT TO BE DEPORTED.

Sir: Gum Boot Charlie, an Alaska native, was discussing the present h. c. l. with a group of citizens of Yakutat, and while condemning the present administration and conditions generally, he was interrupted by a Swede who said: "You dam native, if you don't like this country, why don't you go back where you came from?"

W. W. K.

A Carbondale youth was arrested for hunting out of season, and the possession of a gun and a dog is considered, by the Free Press, "facsimile evidence."

Then, as D. B. B. reminds, there are the writers of apostrophic verse who skip lightly from 'you' to 'thou' and 'thee,' and from 'thy' to 'your.' A language less rugged than the English would have been destroyed long ago.

We learn from the Monticello, Ind., Journal that a couple narrowly escaped being asphyxicated by gas from an anthricate coal stove. Young Grimes must be reporting for that gazette.

Overheard in an osteopath's office: "When does it hurt you most, when you set or when you lay?"

NOTES OF THE ACADEMY OF IMMORTALS.

The following nominations have been received:

For greenskeeper on the Academy links: Mr. Launmore of Pittsburgh. Nom. by S. C. B.

For bugler: Mr. Mescall of Chicago. Nom. by Circle W.

For legal counsel: Atty. Frank Lawhead of Detroit. Nom. by H. D. T.

For any vacancy: Mr. Void Null of Centralia, Mo. Nom. by E. J. C.

MISS SEITSINGER is organizing a chorus and glee club in the schools of Northwood, Ia. Yes, very.

BUTCHER TO THE ACADEMY.

Bill Bull, the Butcher, of Bartlett, Ill.,
Says: "Trade with me. Cut down your bill."
                                        A. G. C.

THE membership committee of the Academy has received numerous protests against the admission of Charles Ranck, the skunk trapper of Ellsworth, Neb., and J. K. Garlick, the "practical horseshoer" of Sublette, Ill.

ACADEMY NOTES.

The nominations were considered of Ananias Deeds of Guthrie Center, Ia., and Mrs. Tamer

Lyons of Upton, Ind. The Academy then resumed work on the Dictionary of Names.

"For goodness' sake!" exclaims Frank Harris
in Pearson's, expressing his joy in the growth of
Lenine's state, "for goodness' sake let us have
new experiments on this old earth." For goodness's sake, let's! But why not have one on a
grand scale? Let's dig a hole a mile deep and a
mile across, fill it with dynamite, and see whether
we can't finish the world in one good bang.

"Learned Class of Europe In Hard Straits."
They are in hard straits everywhere. The more
learned you are, the worse you're off.

"Budapest Hungriest of Cities in all Europe."
—South Bend Tribune.
The headliner must have his little joke.

WE DON'T LIKE TO THINK OF IT!
[From the Cambridge Review.]

Think of the portrait that Rembrandt painted
of his mother hanging in the living-room of his
parents' simple home.

Our blithesome contemporary, F. P. A., is not
disturbed by the steel strike, as he uses a gold pen;
and for a like reason *our* withers are unwrung.
Eugene Field of fragrant memory used a steel

pen. A friend of ours was speaking of having dropped in on the poet just as he was fitting a new pen to the holder. "You can't write anything new," said Field, "unless you have a new pen."

THE SECOND POST.
[Received by a mail order house.]

Dear Sir: The peeaney you shipped me sum time ago come duly recd. My, is we souposed to pay the frate charge onit. When we bot this pee-anney you claimed to lie it down to me. I want you two send me quick as hell a receet for 2.29 for same. Besyds the kees on sum dont work a tall. Is them ivory finger boards. Are dealer here sed we got beet on this deel. Wer is the thing you seet on? Is it eeen that box on the platform at the depo? That luks two small for it. Yours truely, etc.

P. S.—Wen you rite tel me how two tune it.

FIREPLACE heating, says Dr. Evans, is the most wasteful. True. And the most agreeable. So many things that make life endurable in this vale of tears are wasteful.

"SINCE her tour of the Pacific Coast," declares a Berkeley bulletin, "Miss Case has made strident advances in her art." The lady, it appears, sings.

THE SECOND POST.

[Received by a Birmingham concern.]

Dear Sirs and Gents: Would say this lady i got the Range for had applied for a divorce and was to marrey me but she has taken her soldier husband back again and changed her notion so i don't think it right to pay for a range for the other man. let him pay it out if she will live up to her bargin i will pay and could have paid at the time but was afraid this would happen as it has she has never rote or communicated with me since i left there dont think it right or justice that i pay for it and perhaps never see her again had they of rote to me i would have kept up the payments can first see the parties what they expect to do. Very Respect, etc.

You have observed the skinned-rabbit hair-cut. The barber achieves a gruesome effect by running the clippers half-way up the skull. But did you know that it originated in Columbus, O.? "Yes, sir," said the Columbus barber to Col. Drury Underwood, "that started here. We call it the two-piece haircut."

CUPID CARRIES A CARD.

H. H. Lessner, of Alton, Ill., known as "Alton's Marrying Justice of the Peace," carries a union label on his stationery.

"I AM reading Marcus Aurelius now," confides Mme. Galli-Curci to an interviewer. "One can never really grow tired of it, can one?" Well, if you ask us, one can.

"ARE we going crazy?"—Senator Smoot.
"Wanted, man or woman to give me a few lessons on ouija board."—Denver Post ad.
So it seems.

ANNOUNCEMENT!

In accordance with our immemorial custom of giving our readers a Christmas holiday, when it falls on Sunday, the Line-o'-Type will not be published to-morrow.
